PENINSULA

PENINSULA

Published in 2021 by Egg Box Publishing, an imprint of
UEA Publishing Project, University of East Anglia, Norwich
Research Park, Norwich, Norfolk NR4 7TJ
https://www.eggboxpublishing.com/

Peninsula is typeset in Calisto MT
Design and typesetting by Louise Aspinall
Printed and bound in the UK by Imprint Digital
Distributed by NBN International

ISBN: 978-1-913861-31-5

PENINSULA
2021

THE PENINSULA TEAM

Managing Editor: **Amber Kennedy**

Editorial Team: **Sierra Kaag**
Megha Kaul
Sofie Kitts
AM Mac Habee
Lua Morgenstern
Kiera White

Proofreading Editors: **Sierra Kaag**
AM Mac Habee

Publicity Coordinator: **Megha Kaul**

Cover Artwork: **Kiera White**

CONTENTS

POETRY

EDITORS' LETTER

Peninsula is an annual creative writing journal established last year by Durham University Creative Writing Master's Students. This anthology has been produced in collaboration with the Publishing Project Students at the University of East Anglia. This edition primarily includes the works of the 2020-21 creative writing cohort but also features contributions by students across the various different English Studies master's programmes at Durham University.

Over the course of the past year, this group of writers has engaged with each other's styles and interests through the medium of Zoom. For this reason, we have decided to give our edition the theme of The Great Indoors. This is intended to be a testament to the incredible feats of creative productivity which have taken place in isolated rooms before the glare of humming computers.

The editorial team have worked extremely hard to produce this anthology which showcases the talent and craftsmanship of the postgraduate literary sphere at Durham. We hope that you get as much pleasure from reading this diverse collection of works as we have had writing and editing.

Creative Writing Master's Students 2020-21

The story behind our cover art:

In Durham Cathedral's Cloister, you can find a number of interesting characters adorning the ceilings. These Green Men are folkloric figures, often appearing in works of literature, and are regarded as symbols of the life-cycle, springtime rebirth, and creativity itself. This year, the creative writing class of 2021 met entirely via Zoom, with some students unable to visit Durham in person. Peninsula's cover depicts a Zoom class inspired by these foliate figures as a testament to the creativity that has flourished even in the strangest of conditions.

PROSE

Topiary

Something smelled familiar, and it was tugging at Jake's peripheries on Arbor Day. Jake usually possessed an immunity to the smell, but if he hadn't been in the shed for a while the odor resuscitated itself and the thing would catch him mid-headturn, olfactory receptors sneeze-tingling his sinuses, Jake inhaling sharp so's not to lose the memory, eyes searching for a real presence.

It was only a smell.

Smelled like his father's farts, intermingled scents of burnt corn oil, evaporated chemical vapor, and sultry damp. Dook-ends! Plus, Jake had almost glimpsed the apparitional steel toes with the blue Levi's scrunched between the ankle and shoe tongue. He thought of his dad's bare feet. Shoes off, Mister! Nebulous webs and constellations of dark lints mushed into the pale skin. Jake's feet looked different from his father's, too thin to feel kindred.

Jake sat down on the rocking chair. Jake oscillated, swinging feet. Sunlight floored from the shed's two windows and Jake watched the dust chase at itself, disappear, eddy back.

Jake spun a ratchet by the socket piece. Busy-busy. One way and another the handle whirred after he thumbed the gear in the proper direction. He didn't play in the shed often. Today, much-much different.

Jake liked the ratchet. Could feel vibrations of something operating just beneath the metal that seemed unendingly solid. Jake knew more was taking place inside the apparatus than he could articulate, dizzy interworks. It was his father's largest ratchet. The leverage ratchet. Long chrome handle, a dense, heavy head.

***

Sudswater poured into the yellow dish glove. A sucking sound, displacing air. Lani had been playing with her thoughts and the silverware was getting an uneven thrash from the sponge.

She snorted at the moisture submerging her dry skin and caught herself with a smile that was thoughtless and rueful with lip crinkles.

Snorts are for piglets.

She drained the sink, snapped a glove down off her moist hand. She grabbed the blue hand towel. It wouldn't do to have dirty dishes. She shoved the rest of the cutlery in the washer, harder particles still intact, dried her hands anew.

They needed to remember to post-sup rinse.

1:45.

Brysen would be untimely, was untimely.

The girls would be early.

And now she noticed that a splotch of nail polish had frayed up in a soggy moonwane. Unacceptable.

Next.

Working the "Durable, Sturdy Shovel that keeps your hands clean and retrieves effortlessly the pellets and clumps of the litter box," she thought of her mother.

There was an episode she went to.

Look, Momma!, and her mother looking up from a paper stack, red Sharpie rapier bouncing around her mother's students' papers, her mother squinting through thick, scuffed-dull lenses and her mother's owly voice saying, What? And her a little girl with little feet, pursing her lips and turning her cheeks up in her best model-squelch, her mother again owly, saying, What?, A stye?, Are you all right?, with never even a look to her effort, the new-tried makeup from a bag that she, a then-little girl, had stolen from her aunt and had spent time and joy with, her mother unconcerned with both the quality of work and her, the girl with small feet, the shellacked face of a clown.

A stye?

Are you all   right?

Her mother had always put a large space between "all" and "right."

And that was the thing, she thought as she tied the tripled grocery bag, you shouldn't have to explain things to people. Not important things.

The bag went heavy with cat poop.

Not for things that were important, otherwise, what was the point? You could never explain someone into caring. Or into not caring.

That was clever. Maybe she should write that down.

Clever.

Cleverism?

Was that a term?

She snorted.

***

Jake needed both hands to pop the Welch's Grape Soda he pulled from the brittle 1970's mini-fridge. Then, snapity-pop, snapity-pop. Sugar and motion. Nervy contentment. Jake's happy lips dribbled purple soda splotches down his light-grey T, accident.

Leyba was a lump of dead in the middle of the room.

Boring. Bye Felicia.

Jake started thinking on Reyes and Isaiah. He wished Reyes could see him now!

Reyes lived down Jake's street. Reyes and Jake didn't get on well during bus time, but their dads were friends. Sometimes at Reyes' the two boys shot Bullet Balls while their dads got to it, but the two children were each always skittish of each other because neither understood the dual conducts, one set for school and another for home. It was like Jake's mom and dad trying to define BBs.

Two sides.

Always two sides.

Two definitions that at once agreed and disagreed.

It was Jake's mom who said Bullet Balls. Dad would laugh and tell Mom about millimeters until she slapped his butt with something nearby. A magazine. One of Mom's books. Mom's hand. Her foot. Sometimes Mom would laugh and twist Dad's arm up behind him and make Dad slap his own butt with his own hand!

Laughs.

Coos.

Drifting.

Then there would be soft hint-smiles, eyes, for whatever was left of the day. Jake would be set into bed early.

Jake's dad was wrong though, "Bullet Balls" was rebel. Millimeters, c'mon Daddio, math junked.

This one time, Reyes had grabbed Jake as he passed by in the aisle of the bus. Reyes gripped the pressure yields of Jake's nape and pushed Jake to the back, to the double-long seat, hotsticky brown and pleathery.

Reyes smashed Jake's face to the floor and made him lick the scuffed aisleboard.

It was open record, people laughed, molasses bus driver pretending not to notice. Reyes mopped Jakes face back and forth. The ground pebbles and multi-colored castoffs tasted like grains of sand in Jake's mouth. Tears busting down the furrows of red that the floor ridges had indented into Jake's cheeks. The tears were the worst of it. The ground tasted insipid.

Jake drank his Welch's soda, fabricated a fantasy situation that involved Reyes. In daydream Jake gleamed publicly, took out a School Gunman solo.

4 grades older.

Big ol' boy.

While everyone else died red or hid under desks.

After, Reyes deferred to Jake. Gluing up their friendship were many adventures. Cruel giants, fickle elves tucked in the listless curtain sways, severed hairstalks coiled at the tower base. True storied. Up. Up. To cloudcountry.

Reyes and Isaiah were both a grade above Jake. Everything was always happening at the bus. At the last school bell Jake could feel his own blanched moistness, mouth slack down, eyes would keep wide collecting dust boogers. He would get to the bus running, yellow backpack bouncing through the throng, small slaps on his back. Then to the middle seats of the school bus, his cheek on the cool window.

Jake would watch.

Jake would be perceptive and his ability to perceive sandbagged sensations of inadequacy where they were easily sensed.

Same as chewing gum.

Jake watched. Watched with the same intensity that he did when looking through the noisy crack of his parent's bedroom. Long ago times, that.

Here, now, kinda the same thing though.

Isaiah was talking to a group of kids.

Isaiah was gesticulating largely with his hands and Isaiah's peers were listening impatiently, their afterschool machinery ahum. It was a small band gathered in the shady corridor of the parallel school bus.

Isaiah didn't notice Reyes.

Reyes came up behind Isaiah.

The listening children did notice Reyes.

Reyes put a finger vertically to his lips.

Sshhh.

Then creeping, head half taller, bigfat Reyes had Isaiah's neck locked in the crick of his elbow.

Chokehold.

The loose baggage of skin at the bottom of Reyes's orange shirtsleeves hardened as something magmatic rolling into brine, becoming igneous. Like Batista.

Isaiah flailed briefly, arms whipping like pale cartoon ropes.

Everyone was quiet.

Reyes gently helped Isaiah's gravity take him. Isaiah was flat out, not moving. Everyone was watching.

Things slowed for Jake. He had this clamped feeling in his heart and in his genitalia at the same time, something warm and perpendicular in his stomach.

Jake saw the expressions of the children. The expressions were excited. The expressions were worried.

Later.

Jake's mother asking as he sat with chin in the divot of his knees.

What's going on with you, Runk? Gots da runk in your trunk? Maybe you gotsa doo? Runk gotsa doo? Let it out, Runk!

And she was behind him, arms encircling, making tickles at his belly, her raspberry motor-lips at his neck and cheek, tongue as sloppy hog bristle.

Jake squirmed banshee.

Afterwards, breathless, Jake said that he liked movies because they were just like school and his mother laughed and called him, Fatty Runk, Fatty Runk all fatty with a doo.

Made up a stick-note to remind herself to make the Jake play outside more often.

Put stick-note on fridge.

***

The edging was poor on the sidewalk. There was dirt and grass speckled on the concrete. Fernando was strafing the lawn line, leaf-blowing grass tips into the street.

Bry arranged the sod chunks back in patchwork around the new sprinkler head, ground mudded, denim knees mudded, shoes sopped.

Fernando was a kid. 14 years a kid. Fernando's arms and hands shook after laying down the blower. The kid could barely hold the thing.

Good. Good enough anyway. C'mon. We're calling it.

***

Leyba looked like a pile of wadded clothes.

Leyba sprawled between the light from the two windows like a supplicant in front of the shed's door.

Asymmetrical light bookending Leyba's limp form.

The dust motes never seemed to settle.

It was then that Jake noticed his T had a smudge of blackish up by the purple soda stains. He checked the ratchet but there wasn't anything. No blood on the tool.

Jake went back and back in his head. Back to the schoolyard.

Isaiah had started twitching after Reyes had laid him down with the choke. Isaiah's legs and arms and head, vibrated sorta, jerked. And the kids leaned in, a tight necklace around the two forms. Isaiah out and Reyes staid where he was.

Jake could see all of this looking down through the bus window. It would have been real funny to see Reyes afraid. Didn't see though. Too busy seeing Isaiah.

Then Isaiah was up, taut, hinged and springing at the waist. There was a panic in Isaiah's eyes, primal like punched-out wind. Isaiah gasped, then cried for a while and tried to shake it and Reyes came back and tried to soothe Isaiah quiet.

Reyes didn't need the bus monitor to see, the bus monitor who sold gum suckers for a dollar, always from her wrinkled paper bag.

Later.

The bus was in motion and Jake in his own heavy atmosphere.

Isaiah was still explaining things to the crowd, overhanging the seats, dead arms, all unconscious grins and wiggling ears.

It was like dreaming, Isaiah said, I was dreaming, he said, About stealing these shoes but I couldn't run 'cause I forgot to tie them up, The dream seemed to last a really long time, he said, Some other people were there, chasing me for the kix I stoled, right?, That's all I remember, And then I felt myself waking up, but I thought I was waking up in my bed, at home.

Isaiah looked at Reyes. Reyes looked away and smiled without much form.

Then I saw everyone who shouldn't be there, You guys, Isaiah said, and motioned to the other children, It was weird.

Was it a nightmare?, from Joseph in his black and white Raiders, Cry about it some.

There were laughs.

And then it was easy again.

Jake's thoughts, but everyone had been scared when it was happening. Everyone terrified except Isaiah.

***

She was listening for him.

Watching through the foyer window, but also a few paces away from it so he wouldn't glimpse her looking.

She tried to look badly surprised when she opened the door. His truck was loud.

***

Jake probed at Leyba's hair and the back of Leyba's scalp. Leyba's hair was thick, gunked. Dry blood. It was like an end-of-day hairgel.

Blood hairgel. Boss man!

Should have made a mohawk for Leyba before it dried! Too late, Leyba's head wasn't bleeding anymore, wasn't wet. Too dry to be fun!

Jake's thoughts, flesh wound.

Sometimes, like on TV, it took a long time. Sometimes when the knocking out happened, someone would be moved or tied up and wake up in a location far away. Or in the trunk of a car. Or in a jail. Tied up in a burning building, blackest smoke. And everything had been changed, repositioned.

But when you were watching it was quick because it went black on the TV and then it flashed back up, sometimes the sound too, and the image was different. Wasn't what was there before. But it was only quick for the one person, supposition. In real life everyone had to wait around and Jake had just realized that.

It was bore.

Jake had gone up behind Leyba and, and, and… Yassir! Flesh and steel, industry.

Leyba was a real friend. He lived down the street too, but didn't know Reyes. Jake liked that. Leyba went to a different school and his parents were younger than Jake's. Leyba's parents had lots of bright tattoos and wore sweater vests. They were MOABs!

Jake checked Leyba again.

Reyes should be here now. Idiot. Troll. No one in the movies ever choked anyone out. Just knock outs. That was rule. Choke-outs was just in wrestling, and then the other wrestler woke up quick. Reyes was like a wrestler and Jake was like a cop. Jake knew what he was doing with knockouts.

Real serious science.

***

You just can't continue being late, y'know?

Bry grinned. A boy's grin. She loathed that grin. She had to flare her nostrils, a control reflex to keep her lips straight.

You mean, don't be late? Is that really what you mean?

He hasn't been in school today, Bry. I thought it would be nice for the two of you. We can go to a bi-weekly schedule if that's what you need. Is that what you need? Bi-weekly weekends? My obligation ends there. Right exactly there.

Every other weekend? That's what you mean, Lani.

You don't want him on holidays?

I want him holidays. It's not a holiday. It's Arbor Day. Plant a tree for Christ's.

They petitioned it, and Bry, and every parent was into the idea. It's really all out of my hands.

Is that all it takes? Really? A sheet of paper to make a holiday? You didn't sign it?

The school mails it. No. I didn't sign it. You're drinking.

Thank God for that.

Lani walked to the Dodge.

He listened to the clack of her heels, a spent chamber sound. He thought she must be listening to it too. Listening, but not just listening, accentuating, aware of her sound. He loved her calves, milked-grey at the muscle lines.

Her skirt a blue lick at the back of her knees. Even after the pregnancy, Lani went right back to form. Conversely, her mother was melted lumps and buttah bean-bags.

Lani pulled a Pauli's bottle from his truck, displayed it, turned it over, shook out the liquid.

It smells like weed, Bry. What the hell? You're going to drive him around like that?

When Lani looked up from the citrine beer puddle, she was alone outside.

Lani checked the living room. There was motion in the kitchen. The dishwasher was open, and he was holding two mismatched teacups and a pint of Beam.

Lani tossed the Pauli bottle into the trash.

This isn't yours anymore.

She waved her arms about like there were acoustics above her.

Yeah.

You can't come in without asking.

Yeah.

Your cell? Why have it, right? It just rings.

It's in the truck.

On Friday, that's smart. Real smart. Really good. What if I were a client, Bry?

Silence.

Then.

He held the cup out too fast, with little laps up the side. He twisted the bottle cap up and returned the Beam to his back pocket. He liked the way Lani gripped her cup, roseate fingernails.

He wanted her to comb and scour his skin the same color as those nails.

Bry rubbed at that jaw-ball below his ear. Put his thumb up under it, rubbed thoughtfully.

Can I throw my grass bags here?

You have a dumpster.

I was late.

You are late.

I showered.

Her smile was getting better and her eyes did this neat, oversaturated thing. They drank some more Beam. They got brighter and brighter, burnished, really.

They went outside to smoke. They leaned against the front bumper of his truck.

Nicotine had a strong orbital effect because each had quit smoking, each proving something that they had never been able to do together. They took some drags. Then she held the cigarette in limbo. For a long time her hand didn't move and neither person said anything. Drifting plumes. They were halfway in the sun. It seemed a spacious area even though it was not. A tight, enclaved corridor of the few simple feet between the truck and the garage door. It was pleasant. It was warm, infusing.

Why is it like this?

Like?

Lani paused and took in some smoke. Then she stayed paused. Then not.

I'm sorry. I'm really sorry. You don't even know.

Apologies? Aren't those for people who think you have more for them? Or is it when they think you have nothing.

You're drunk.

Still.

He looked at her sideways and grinned and she looked lackadaisical, straight on at him, until she couldn't and looked away. Then he took the low cigarette from between her fingers.

***

Gathered water pinched from Jake's eyes into tears, fell on Leyba's cheek, rivulets streaked out of sight. Leyba didn't react, didn't move.

It had been too long.

Please wake up.

Shit, Captain, are we good?

Jake put his mouth on Leyba's mouth. Jake pinched Leyba's nose shut. Jake pushed hard air through his cheeks. Wasn't working well.

No one would know. No one could know. Leyba's wet lips.

People shouldn't never know about Jake's mistake. Jake didn't know what people would do. Beyond his ken. Jake felt that surely. Duh, duh, dumb dumb.

The reprimand about Leyba would be something real. Worse than Hell.

Maybe Hell. What the hell was Hell? Jake knew that he would be alone. That would be a large part of it.

I don't want to be alone.

Jump.

Pop up like Isaiah.

Like vampires at night.

Jake again put his lips on Leyba's let his lungs into Leyba's mouth. Leyba's cheeks bulged. Jake's ears popped. Just a little pop. Some air went into Leyba, not much air. Jake rose, pushed at Leyba's chest with open hands but it didn't feel like Leyba's chest was going in and Jake fitted his fingers together, hands big ol' fist, pounded down on Leyba's ribs. Pounded.

Jake hovered his ear to Leyba's nose and felt air. Leyba was breathing. Stupidhead. Jake already knew that. Leyba was supposed to be breathing better now, stirring, like after the lifeguards came.

Jake shook Leyba by the shoulders, Leyba's head wheeling loose like a child feigning sleep. Only no hidden grin, not fluttering blinders. Jake slapped Leyba, twice. Wiped snot. Re-pounded chest.

Notscience. What now?

Jake bit his own hand, the loose skin between his thumb and index, and meant to chomp all the way through. The pain stopped him fast though. Thoughts, new pain doesn't really stop other kinds of pain. People only create new pain to show off. Shit, shit.

Then Jake sat holding his own knees and looked down at Leyba. Every detail was arresting and for a moment Jake couldn't stop tracing the topography of the other boy's face.

Leyba was smooth, tan for summer, eyelids calm cause he wasn't faking, nostrils serene and moving in cadence. Leyba's velvet-polish forehead brushed by dishwater bangs, frizzy. But a tangled mess at the sides, a gradient to the dark crust-strings hanging at the back.

Everything had a murmur. The walls and floor moved in and out.

So Jake just sat with those large, afterschool eyes. Jake sat. Jake looked.

***

It was one of those things he always thought about after fucking her.

She snorted, intake snorts, impassioned snorts. But it was a definite pattern of snorts.

When they were new to each other, she couldn't achieve orgasm after he heard her snort. And she was a constant snorter. She apologized every time for the snorts and the lack of climax, I'm sorry, Just a little piggy, It's just something, Something, I don't know, I like it though, You, You know?, I feel the borders of it, the shape of it, It's good, Does that make sense?, It just won't go, It's not you, You know that?

The way afterwards, that she put her head on his armpit and would nuzzle up his lean anteriors, tickles, he could feel the humid warmth of breath, her face going up into his armpit, smelling deeply, little toothy bites on the way back down. The enwrapment of toes.

It had changed. Now she was uninhibited and constrictive. Proud snorts, proud orgasms.

Lani thought about all different things after.

The girls are coming.

Hmmm.

C'mon, Bry.

Bry checked his discarded Levi's. The Beam pint was empty.

Downstairs he poured whiskey from the cupboard. Crown. He put on the dishwasher. He heard the vacuum go on upstairs.

***

His boots were steel toed, and rough camel-tan leather with thick-rubber soles.

Work boots.

She had bought those boots.

They had a Puma Logo on each of the tongues. Bry still only had everything that she had picked out for him.

There were dirt sprinkles around the boots. Little chunks of richdark soil already into the half-shag carpeting.

Bry had showered before he got there and cleaned up a stubble shape sans neckbeard, black and thick, changed his clothes, deodorant, chopped the nails, even the toes, and combed his hair. And put the day's long work boots back on over new socks.

She launched the work boots down the stairs and reprimanded herself for the dirt that must be at the bottom of the flight for the impact.

Then the vacuum. She worked it over everything, hitting and ricocheting off furniture legs. Back and forth. Back and forth.

His lifestyle was showing. Was he aware?

The enlarged pores bubbling at his nose? And deepening eyes? He was quite brown and rust spotted at the temples too; the damage of the sun. She could see him in flashes, these comparison, side-by-side pictures and it hurt.

One image young. One image now.

Bry ravened for constant stimulations of any sort. Espresso, lotto tickets, liquor, snowboarding, cigarettes, video games, sex, pushups, mastrabation.

One of her friends had mentioned the term furious mastrabation.

Bry's breathing was never shallow.

When Bry was alone he was a splayed-out state of exhaustion that anyone, anyone would have said was a vermillion flag. Beaten was Bry's normal. His backstage from the Cheshire proscenium that was his life.

Cleverisms?

She found him like that sometimes, when Bry didn't hear her approach, usually in the Lay-Z-Boy with the lights out, lit pale by the TV glow. He was naked in the raw, pulsing, like muscle burned too far gone to let the host sleep. And she would have awful dreams.

Their therapy sessions eroded in Bry's laughter.

Bry said, A-n-a-l-ysis when he talked about therapy.

Her mother had liked Bry. Bry the pallbearer of her mother's ashes to the river fork. Bry holding the faux-ivory urn tenderly, loose and balanced as a school-project egg. Bry's expression was an unconscious smile. He didn't mean it, the smile, he just didn't know how to do it otherwise.

Her and her sparse family had all walked the dirt road that paralleled the brown river. A lane of blue sky overhead trampled on the sides by black trunks, swaths of oak foliage. The road was grey with slurpysucking mud.

She had watched her mother's ashes and felt a vague anger under her lower ribs.

Smatterings of grey diffusing like magician birthday powder, sputtering in the cool air. Yellow clumps falling and going down the river like gobs of wet flour.

Bry wasn't anywhere when everyone was starting up their cars and when she walked back down the road to get him, she knew.

Bry was walking up the road, small steps, still smiling in the leaf-dappled sunshine.

About his eyes a splotchy red hue.

She wondered if he had ever cried sober.

She had been over the bedroom three times now with the vacuum. She stopped, breathed.

Breathed.

Breathed and slammed the vacuum into the closet and watched a piece of the textured sheetrock crumble and indent around the handle.

Unacceptable.

She straightened herself. She made up the bed.

***

The trash bags had a fumesmell: gooey sunwarm bacteria and deadheaded organics. He grabbed six full, three in each hand, up and out of the bed of his truck.

He felt this neat breeze pass through him and the clouds rattled gently above.

The neighborhood was a temporal place. Most the structures were age-bevelled brick, houses with downtrodden yards surrounded by vagrant businesses.

A neophyte investor had been optimistic, built their house new. A corner house. The loan price reflected the overeagerness of the construct, bright white siding and tar shingles.

There were marvelous evenings around move in. Wine and take-out. Moving boxes topped by pillowcases as makeshift tables, candles in green beer bottles. Naked skin on puffy carpeting. Everything smelling of new lacquer. His brown arms dense on her paleness.

So much room.

Now

The dumpster was empty. He set the bags in it.

His patio chair was gone. There was another now. Plastic, blue. He loved sitting here. Loved watching. Clouds, strong wind, movement.

Back then, he used to sit, his pores stinging from work, mushy from the shower, scalding. With a whiskey. Watch the changes. Dusk. Really trying to notice the melt, the convolution. You had to linger to see the shadows stretch.

His footfall was too heavy when he left the sidewalk and he had to use corrective steps for equilibrium.

He looked in the shed window but it was all sunshine glare.

***

4:30.

The girls were coming. One after another then another. Like Bag End. Her mother had loved that book.

Like the bag's end.

How was that, Mother?

They, the girls, they all slept at her house.

She had just hung up with Leyba's parents.

Jake's dad is late. Again. I'll send Leyba home before Jake leaves, unless you need him now? No?

Leyba's parents were irritating, always with those calm, slow voices, like they possessed a vast aquifer of wisdom. They also had a tendency to repeat what the other had said, but with a slightly different intonation of voice.

She had seen Bry outback in his socks, wandering about with bandy legs, holding his face up to the sky with his eyes closed and inhaling.

These gatherings always happened at her house.

You live the closest to downtown, The shortest drive from the bars, The good bars, We can run with the best of them, too, You too, You're the best of us, Wild-hearted, Where's Bry at nowadays?

She had Jake's weekend bag done. It was a large green duffle.

She got out the Crown and took a slug. She noticed the salmon rack when she put the bottle back in the cupboard, "The difference in the lives of millions of happy women and their husbands and family...and their weight." The rack was designed to separate the flesh from fat? Buy salmon for the fat. Brain food, diet food, relentless fucking spawning food.

Then she smelled it. The cat had taken one of those mammothmountain shits.

***

Bry's puke was controlled into a tight projectile. He had sprayed "quick-diffusing, slow-fading, fragrance emulsifiers" in the room. Turned fart fan switch. Sprayed outside.

He didn't see Lani when he came out. Good. Saw Jake.

The boy, Jake, Jake Runk! was a strange color. Jake looked pale and orange, splotchy.

One, two, here we go.

He straightened, managed well. He walked without sway. He was allowed to be exhausted, he worked, boy knew that. Tired, like a streetlight.

Oh, he had fallen a bit into the couch. He motioned for the boy. When the boy got there, he put his arm around him.

How was your day, Runk? You got free hook-ie from the hippies. They wanted you to plant trees. I did it enough for both of us. We should have gone fishing. Fishing tomorrow, Runkage?

Jake nodded.

I'm ready now, Dad.

Yeah, me too. Where are you, Mom?

The word Mom came out grizzled. Winced at the sound.

Got out his cell phone. They could take turns. Oh, oh, oh. Hated phones. Small finger touches.

Here. Find us a game, Runk.

***

She set the duffle bag in the foyer. The two of them were on the couch. Warm, afternoon light lit up the room.

There was the shittysingsong of a cellphone game.

She felt roused embers working in her. Bry could be so good when he wanted to; he wasn't strict, but loyal and understanding. He walked by his son; he wasn't a scout.

What did that even mean?

Her mother's metaphors and analogies and stupidschool brain never let her explain herself properly.

She frowned. That's why Jake went to him. For comfort. For assurance. Jake went to her for something else, lists and itineraries of elses. That was parenting, that's what spawning was. Upstream to death. What the hell was a matter with her? How could she think like this and cry quietly, suppressing broken giggles, when Jake laid his curly brown hair on her lap?

She took a slug off of the Crown.

Someone had to rub ointment into Jake's cuts and scrapes. Was it fun? Could a bee sting be fun? The red-bleeding, scratched-off heads of mosquito bites? Attentiveness wasn't fun.

The whiskey went down hard, she swallowed twice.

What did he do to the kitchen?

I can smell it everywhere. You can't drink without vomiting now? Is that supposed to be an example? Jake, where's Leyba?

He walked home.

Good. It's time. Tracks, Brysen, tracks. Now.

Bry pivoted his neck, his face above the black of the pleather couch. He was ruddy and it took a minute for his blue eyes to hold her face.

And then she was covering the distance. Clack, clack, clack. She was overhead and she saw that Jake was looking down, all his attention in that game.

She slapped the top of Bry's head. She meant to slap the top of his head but her palm landed on the upperside of his forehead: half forehead, half eye. One eye bulged with irritated water.

The hell, Bry? You have to go. Now.

It was her whisperhiss.

C'mon, Runk. Let's go for a drive. My navigator, huh? Watch my four?

Bry looked back up at her and warbled his head in some poor imitation of a shake. He was hurt. He was reprimanding her.

Unacceptable.

He said it fondly.

Don't be such a butt-shark.

***

Jake didn't feel the tugs at his arm. The tugs were random in rhythm. A tow-and-drift routine captioned by the stumbles and corrections of his father.

Jake was dimly aware of his dragging shoes, the tile grout-spaces grabbing at the soles of his Vans shoes.

His parents were yelling.

They had to wait in the foyer so Dad could put on his shoes. After the first try standing, Dad sat down and closed one eye to tie the shoestrings up.

Dad almost forgot the overnight bag. Mom called at Dad from the threshold and he went back to the entryway for it. Jake could hear them through the vehicle's window glass.

Dad was at the door and Mom was looking out through the crack.

It's easy, isn't it? To tell your friends? Every weekend?

You're drunk.

It's easy to define someone else from a distance. You can do it, my whole thing. I don't give a shit. Your fucking words.

Stop. Listen Bry. Quiet. Shhhh. Please. Just drive home. I don't want my friends to see you like this. They ask me. What am I supposed to say? Huh? They ask me. Us girls love to hash it out over dinner. Dinner's all I got. Sure.

That stopped Dad. He swayed.

You know you ain't going to dinner. That's not where you're going. Girls don't eat dinner together. Nobody *just* eats dinner together.

Leave.

Say you ain't going to dinner.

Leave.

Say it. I'll leave.

You will leave.

And Mom shut the door.

Dad took a large rock, stippled white, out of the border of one of the flowerbeds. The misplaced stone left a small crater with rooty edges. Dad hurled the rock through the kitchen window.

They eased out of the driveway. There was breathing and silence.

***

It was quiet in the bar when Lani turned her phone back on.

They were at a post-stop, done with the clubs. The girls and her all smelled like tepid beach sand and they were dazed and exhausted.

It was the last dimmydive that was opened.

A moaning swamp cooler was helping her shiver off club sweat.

When she got the phone call, she answered. She listened and looked in the large bar mirror. She thought she saw a flickering at the edges. But by then she had stopped looking, stopped listening. She wanted more space from the room.

***

Jake was awake in his blankets. Blossomed and awake. Jake felt like a wormhole, the circumference of his world and its atmosphere the exact line of an event horizon. The world was passing through him but suspended also. Like the Discovery Channel. Information. Artifacts squared.

Jake had walked the world away from the grasp of others. He felt Leyba. Like through glass. Underwater. Not friends, but conjoined. There was no such concept as travel, just an aperture.

In the shed, Jake had pulled a tarp from beneath the roughcut workbench. The tarp was blue. There were lacquer splotches on it.

Jake had spread the tarp out on the floor and pulled Leyba by the feet until Leyba was sprawled on it. Then Jake collected up the excess corners in his hands. Jake drug the whole thing into the corner. Sounds like snow-pants.

Jake wanted to leave something with Leyba. Something of his. Something like the Bullet Ball gun. But Jake didn't have anything.

Jake had held his hand on top of Leyba's mouth and nose for a time. Jake had counted, tried to get to five minutes, but he had lost count.

Had he lost the count too long or too short?

Jake brushed his lips on Leyba's forehead, then had tucked edge of tarp loose around the head.

Then it was done and Jake had left.

And now it was now and someone was yelling. Someone was yelling. The door was locked. Someone kicked it. Someone kicked at it and the door rattled. Jake didn't know if it was his dad kicking or the police kicking or if there was a difference. No privacy in his crack. And Jake didn't know if he was in his bedroom or if he was in the shed. Jake was in both the shed and his bedroom. Jake didn't know if he was Jake or Leyba. It was dark. Not lonely. Just dark. It was just dark with strobes of light banging through the creases of the shivering doorframes. Everything was concerned. The light coming in was both a particle and a wave. The audience was there. Jake was watching them watch something that was him but was also outside of his proprioception. The sounds of everything continued.

end.

La Cucaracha

His eyes water in the cold air as he swings *back'n'forth, back'n'forth.* The toes
of his worn sneakers drag across the gravel, which has a pleasant roughness,
like the surface of a scab newly forming. The playground and patch of
dead grass dubiously labelled "Morris Square Park" is nearly empty, as it
naturally would be early on a Tuesday afternoon, a school day, when the
children of East Harlem should all be ensconced in classrooms, their heads
busily bent over algebra or social studies. Years later, he will wonder why
he didn't question all the missed days of school, his mother simply saying
in her typically vague way "Matteo stays home today." He'll never really
understand her use of the third person when referring to him, but eventually
he will decide to interpret this as her un-spoken way of constructing him in her
mind, her attempt to announce his reality to herself and the rest of the world.

She stands now by the climbing frame, her hand resting on the ladder to
the slide, wrapped in the faded tweed coat she found at a thrift store in the
days when she still ventured out into the world, a shapeless lump against the
grey November sky. She faces away from him, but he knows she is wearing
the same blank expression she always wears, that of a whiteboard just
erased. If his seven-year-old brain still cooking up emotional intelligence
could grasp the feeling of resentment, he would feel it. As it stands, he feels
only the transitory contentment that "child-on-swing" always feels.

The "patch-of-dead-grass-called-park" is empty apart from Matteo, his
mother, an uppity-looking woman walking her dog, and a sleeping bag
lying horizontal on a bench which Matteo imagines must contain one of the
homeless people he knows from teachers and television not to talk to. He
quickly tires of the swing—the relentless *back'n'forth, back'n'forth* becoming
less comforting and more cloyingly hypnotic—and hops off the cold plastic
seat. Aimlessly, he wanders over to a patch of dirt in a corner created by low
moss-covered walls that surround this "patch-of-dead-grass-called-park",
picks up a stick and begins to draw squiggly patterns in the mud. He sees a
hole and, unthinkingly, pokes at it.

Out of it scuttles a brown insect, the same colour as the dirt, long
antennae inquisitively swaying *back'n'forth, back'n'forth.* He feels no fear, only

fascination. Careful not to startle it, he bends down to get a closer look at this brand-new life form. It moves quickly, its legs pumping as its flat back shifts this way and that like a leaf blowing in the wind, constantly changing directions as if uncertain which way it should be going.

Ignoring the little voice in his head that tells him he shouldn't get his clothes all muddy, Matteo lays down fully on his stomach and scootches forward. The creature, who was heading towards him, freezes in place except for the occasional twitch of an antenna. Matteo wonders if it is wondering what he is too, with his big clumsy seven-year-old body and his wrinkled nose inches from its tiny head. But then it turns and skitters away, through the mud and into the welcoming darkness of a pile of dead leaves. He does not know its name, but he is struck by its speed, its movement, its alive-ness, the fifth being present in this "patch-of-dead-grass-called-park" in The Centre of New York in The Centre of The World in The Centre of The Universe, The Centre of which is this insect without a name and Matteo, which is him. Then his mother is standing next to him, still looking straight ahead, and telling him to get up because they are going home. She says nothing about the mud on his sweater.

Five years later, the school bell rings. Matteo marches out to a picnic table in the playground, armed with the peanut-butter-and-strawberry-jelly sandwich he made himself that morning and his science teacher's "The Big Book of Bugs". This is his lunchtime ritual. While the other children shriek, or play tag, or merely stand in groups whispering about their dawning realisation that some of them are girls and some of them are boys and that this carries with it some meaning they don't yet quite understand, he eats and reads about Goliath beetles and vampire moths and red-legged grasshoppers, studying the Latin names and biological diagrams with concentration. His favourite page contains information about the insect he now knows is called a cockroach, from the Spanish *cucaracha,* of the order Blattodea, which derives from the Latin *blatta,* meaning "insect that shuns the light". While his teachers complain about his inability to focus on his classes, writing letters home that are never opened, he can recite by heart the cockroach's unimaginably long history, dating back 320 million years. He has read more times than he can remember about its ability to survive stomping, poisoning, beheading, nuclear apocalypse. He notices them everywhere, scuttling between the feet of rushing commuters on the subway and lurking beneath the rusty pipes of sinks in public bathrooms. They are a strangely comforting constant to him, with his sightings separating the dull years that would otherwise blur together.

When he had spotted the tell-tale black smudge in the corner of his math classroom two years ago, half the kids had climbed up onto their desks in terror screaming "get it out, get it out!" They had thought Matteo was a hero for carefully catching the insect in his rolled-up quiz paper, but really, he had just wanted to make sure the poor thing didn't get stomped on. Instead of flushing it down the toilet, he had shaken it onto the lawn outside and watched it pause for a moment before scuttling away. Last year, he'd found one hiding behind the couch while he was looking for his lost Iron Man action figure. The toy had been a birthday present from his father, sent in the mail with the customary yearly card that expressed the hopes that he was "being a good boy and not giving your mother any trouble." The postmark said California. He'd long before learned to stop asking why his father lived in California instead of with him and his mother in their cramped one-room apartment. He'd had a creeping fear his mother had thrown the action figure away, but when he looked behind the couch there it was, covered with several weeks' collection of dust and with an inquisitive cockroach perched on top like a bow, its antennae swaying *back'n'forth, back'n'forth*.

He had thought for a moment about showing it to his mother. He thinks he remembers her long ago, when she was different to how she is now, tucking him into bed and singing a strange little song that went

"La cucaracha, the cockroach, can't walk anymore.

Because it doesn't have, because it's missing, Two little back legs.

When a boy loves a girl, and she doesn't love him back,

It's the same as if a bald man finds a comb on the railroad track.

La cucaracha, the cockroach, can't walk anymore.

Because it doesn't have, because it's missing, Two little back legs."

By the time she reached the end of the song, he would have nearly sunk into sleep, but would still be awake enough to feel the gentle brush of her soft lips against his forehead. Matteo shook his head and glanced over the back of the couch. His mother was standing on their tiny balcony, half hidden behind a line of washing, the smoke from her cigarette winding away and disappearing into the growing darkness of evening. Her eyes were fixed on the city skyline. With its collection of little lit up windows, it looked as fake as a cardboard cut-out. He decided to trap the cockroach in a glass and carry it downstairs instead.

Eight years later, Matteo is sweating as he carefully manoeuvres a box down three flights of stairs, thinking about where it will fit in the already packed truck he has parked outside. He is hoisting the box into an available space when his cell phone interrupts him with its shrill ringing. He answers the phone and holds it to his ear, listening through the crackly static of the poor reception you always get just inside the gates of the apartment complex. He thinks he hears "wooden," then "widow," then "we're done," followed by words that sound like "I'm sorry" and "I loved you," though they might as well be "misery" and "I'm tired of you." He doesn't respond; because he doesn't believe it, because he doesn't know what to say, because he simply doesn't want to. Instead, he puts his phone back in his pocket and goes upstairs to get the final box. As he lifts it into his arms, a skittering noise and a whir of wings startles him enough that he tilts the box sideways, allowing a picture that was balanced on top to slip out. There is a second of silence as it falls, then the shattering of glass, then silence again, disturbed only by a faint skittering, scampering, scurrying. He nearly drops the box in his haste to pick up the picture. It shows a smiling couple, the woman holding a chubby cheeked baby in her arms, laughing at nothing. He carefully dusts off the shards of glass, places the picture and its now mangled frame back into the box, and then turns to the noise that had caused all this in the first place.

The culprit is none other than a cockroach, from the Spanish *cucaracha,* of the order Blattodea, which derives from the Latin *blatta,* meaning "insect that shuns the light". Only now, in the empty apartment, it has nowhere to hide. With surprising speed, it scuttles *back'n'forth, back'n'forth* along the floor next to the wall, desperately seeking the only shelter it can find in the bare room, its shiny brown body standing out like a sore thumb against the wash of grey that is wall and carpet. A prickle goes up the back of Matteo's neck at the sound. And suddenly he is filled with burning anger, because how dare this pest live here rent free all these years, how dare it occupy the only song he can remember his mother singing, how dare it survive stomping, poisoning, beheading and nuclear apocalypse while his own mother bent to the pressures of the world and then soundlessly snapped, like a branch in a forest when no one's around to hear. He reaches out his hand to grasp it between thumb and index finger, its legs flailing and antennae quivering. He takes one delicate barbed leg between his fingers and pulls. There is slight resistance, but then it comes away cleanly, and an inexplicable feeling of comfort washes over him, as if his mother is once more singing,

La cucaracha, the cockroach, don't complain, it'll do no good
Can't walk anymore, poor skittering thing,
Because it's missing, because I've pulled off
Two little back legs.
How lame, how tame, the shame it must feel
At cockroach thanksgiving
Dragging itself 'round over the ground
On only three feet, thoroughly beat,
Painfully reliving,
the cockroach, the mock-roach.
When a boy loves a girl, and she doesn't love him back
It's the same as if the mock-roach
Finds four back shoes he cannot use,
A memento of his lack
The cockroach, the mock-roach, making all the children laugh.
Only one foot left, what will you do
Not so indomitable now, are you?

An English Distance

I.

I couldn't remember what day it was. Amongst the blankets and pillows my mind fumbled to get a grip on the hours that silently slipped by. They looked so alike I couldn't tell one from the other, each possessing more or the less the same drudgery. As the days flitted by, my mind felt like the rotting apple that sat on my windowsill, destined to shrink into itself and go dull and brown with each passing second.

I peeked my head out from the covers and looked at the clock on my bedside table. Almost 1PM. The hand seemed to tick loudly and incessantly. It reminded me of the metronome my primary school piano teacher used while I was playing. I think it was supposed to keep me in time. It didn't work. I think I ended up quitting after less than a year.

Mum knocked at my bedroom door, interrupting my reverie. She entered to see me lying in bed, my eyes half-open, staring at the clock.

"You up, honey?"

"Yes," I replied, and turned to the window instead. The sun bleared into my room and onto the apple, its rays dim and pale to reflect its own uncertainties over the prospect of a summer. I had forgotten to close the curtains last night.

"What are you thinking about doing this afternoon?"

"It'll be a busy one. I was thinking of closing the curtains. Then I'll get a cup of tea, come back to my room and stop my clock."

As I waited for her reply my eyes turned to *Mrs Dalloway,* lying next to said clock. I grabbed the copy, held it to my chest and worried the spine like a loose tooth. I could hear the chimes of Big Ben in 1920s London clanging in my head.

Mum had been looking at her phone in that particularly frustrating way middle-aged people do, unable to take anything else in as her fingers blundered across the keyboard. The woman never listens to me.

"That's nice, honey. I need you to help me with the grocery shopping. We'll leave in an hour."

With that she turned and left, but not before she left my door open. I tumbled out of bed, my limbs stiff with inertia, feeling old and sorry for myself. There was nothing to do, but if I didn't wish to retire to my bedroom for the foreseeable future, the sun reminded me that I could sit outside. Old people do that, don't they? They don't wait for death in a darkened room. No, they wake up, then sit outside until 4PM when it's time for dinner, and then they go to bed. Perhaps a bit of *Midsummer Murders* in between. Then they wake up and begin the farce again. I wish I could do that. It would be appropriate, with my youth dissolving like sugar in a hot cup of tea.

I promise that I'm not tone-deaf, by the way, just dramatic. Even my middle-class brain knew that to be stuck inside a semi-detached house on a tidy suburban street was a privilege. But knowing this didn't help, and my self-pity and guilt hardened together into a thick, impenetrable crust.

I shut the door.

II.

In the queue to get into the supermarket, Mum craned her head to see if she could spot any deals on ready meals. I think scouring shops for half-prices and three-for-twos was a ritual to keep the world from falling in on her. I stood beside her aimlessly, gazing at one of the stickers the staff had placed on the floor, signalling that everyone ought to stand the width of two trollies apart. A pair of toddlers squealed behind me, their mother on the phone, unaware that her children weren't abiding by the trolley rule. They were yelling about the myriad of badly drawn rainbows that littered the walls near me. Jaded, I got out my phone and opened the first app my eyes fell on.

A tagging-challenge à la 2011... Workout video... #*TBT! Wish I was back in Greece right now*... Workout video... *The UK is coming together in this time of crisis, we are so proud of this nation and Boris Joh—*

It was relentless. I rolled my eyes, closed the app, and put my phone back in my pocket.

I tried to avoid thinking about shopping, lest my mind wander to the empty shelves inside, which never failed to send a shot of anxiety into my veins. Instead I looked to my right, to an empty Costa, spotting a young man and woman, presumably a couple, chatting to one another. Two metres apart, of course. They were talking so animatedly that it disheartened even me, usually a despiser of PDA, to see the lack of physical affection they could give to one another. How starved of intimacy and unused to touch would we be after all this? The social norms would be like something out of a Jane Austen novel.

I pictured two forty-year-old women, adorned in nineteenth-century garb, their hair in ringlets and hands in white gloves, carrying parasols. They were taking some air in the grounds of Chatsworth House, gossiping vivaciously to one another. A lapdog scampered behind them.

"Did you hear? The young Miss Harriet brushed hands with a Costa barista the other day when getting her morning coffee. If you ask me, it was quite the scandal. Imagine exposing herself in such a manner... and with gloveless hands! What must her family think!"

Perhaps that English politeness foreigners naively assumed we had would be back in style. Personal space would be well-regarded while "I hope your family is in good health" would punctuate every email.

"You can go in now," a shop assistant called to Mum, and she pushed the trolley indoors. I dawdled behind her.

III.

It had been later than planned, but I had drawn the curtains, fetched a cup of tea and stopped my clock. But when I settled down in bed to wait for nothing my phone lit up and started ringing. Video call.

On calls in the past my friends and I had conducted pub quizzes and would get drunk while doing so, and for the most part, it was fun. But I dreaded that moment when you said goodbye, shut off your laptop and were in your room, head spinning and heart racing, alone. It's a very sudden, overwhelming feeling of loneliness, because even if you've been lonely all week you've gotten used to it, only to be granted a temporary pardon and then for the feeling to suddenly swallow you again, teeth and all.

My heart started to beat rapidly, coinciding with the consecutive beeps of the phone, until I heard Mum shout for me from below.

"Honey, would you like to come downstairs? The clapping's about to start."

It was comical to watch the inhabitants of my street leave their houses every Thursday evening to bellow and clap for the NHS. As they were mostly Conservative supporters, I found it droll that these people who had been voting to cut the funding of free healthcare were now singing its praises.

"No thanks, I'm on the phone," I shouted back, while simultaneously ending the call that was still buzzing.

I also didn't want to go downstairs and see my family. I found my mum daft, but she was mostly harmless. It was my dad and siblings who I frequently argued with. I could hear them squabbling downstairs already. It's stupid, petty stuff, but it got to me because of the nagging tug of regression at my sleeve. After all, I spent most of the year at university, only coming back for the odd weekend, even in the summer. Now I was stuck at home, fighting with my family again as if I were fifteen.

I lay down in my bed and tried to go to sleep.

IV.

I woke up a couple of hours later with a feeling of clarity. The sky had grown dark and the streetlights a burnt orange, but I had one desperate craving, and that was to be outside. It was May, so still warm. I was ready in less than five minutes and slammed the door behind me.

Despite the balminess, there weren't many outside lingering on thresholds like I was. Even the soft wind felt quiet and forlorn, as if I could search within it and find only wispy emptiness. I stuck my headphones on and made a split decision to walk past the river, seeing as I hadn't been there in a long time.

I passed some flats and was reminded suddenly of an article that had been floating around social media that described social distancing as Edward Hopper paintings. It was particularly noticeable when looking at these little windows, seeing the lights on and people bustling about indoors, getting ready for bed. They were so close to each other, but not quite.

As I approached the river, I saw that the streetlights that surrounded it made the water glitter, while the anchored boats swayed peacefully atop it, fashioning the city I usually detested into something almost scenic. If you forgot about the empty crisp packets and faint smell of weed, of course. Either way, I was suddenly awash with a memory from last year, where my friends and I had sat at the edge of the water, a little drunk after being in the pub, messing around and chatting about next summer. I could remember an exchange between the six of us, almost word for word.

"It's going to be amazing. We'll have just finished our exams, and we'll spend our days celebrating—"

"Drinking!"

"—Celebrating *and* drinking all across Europe!"

"You say that as if I've studied."

"Forgot you were dumb."

"I have ADHD!"

"Shut up, or I'll push you in the river."

"You won't, I've just washed my hair!"

And so on, I thought, smiling to myself.

I took my headphones off and decided to sit down at the water's edge for a while. It was mercifully quiet. For once the memory had not consigned me to an hour of melancholy but had comforted me. I knew that the inescapable feeling of ensnarement would return when I went back home, fierce as ever, but for now it had abated. May melted in my mouth. Everything seemed soaked with impermanence.

On leaving your childhood home and getting your first real job

It's a funny thing, leaving the house you grew up in. Doesn't really matter what kind it was. Always thought mine was fairly standard, which doesn't mean exactly average but you know, not unusual either. It wasn't one of those identikit, Playmobil houses anyway. You know the ones – a bunch of stark rows of identical roofs marooned in a field or off some road. Playing at being houses. Not enough cupboard space in those things – God knows how you are supposed to manage. But my house was normal enough. It had a kitchen that everyone always complained was slightly too small. A dining room which was only used at Christmas. A bedroom each. Standard fare. "Characterful," said the estate agent. "Spacious rooms," occasionally "it's a very quiet road." Then the prospective buyers would all nod nervously and flee back to their own cars to discuss it in private. Nobody likes to criticise a house where they might be overheard.

They were useless anyway, the estate agents. No sense of the important stuff. The way the wind howls through the cupboards upstairs when its blowing at a certain angle. The beam with all the chunks missing like something took a bite out of it – two bites. The acrylic carpet that melted rather than burned when someone forgot to turn off their hair-straighteners. Not even the stuff you'd think they'd lap up. Like the second staircase – the really grand one that sweeps all the way from the top landing down to the door. Real selling-point that. I mean – sure – you can only go down those stairs, and they aren't actually visible when you're not standing on them, and it can be pretty difficult to find the top of them as well. But still, I'd think there's a hell of a lot more appeal there than "original oak doors." Think of the sunlit hall with the lead-paned windows. Actually, even I only found that one the once in twenty-two years of living there, so maybe I can understand why it isn't part of their little tour. Same goes for the neat sun-dappled courtyard garden you can see from some of the windows, but which doesn't seem to have an entrance. And I suppose a lot of the passageways can only be found at night which wouldn't have worked with an 11am viewing.

No one ever came after nightfall. Downright irresponsible that. How are you supposed to know a house you haven't seen in the dark?

The true dark, which is any room once the sun has gone down. Any room in which you have been left alone with the things that lurk. Not being chaperoned by some spotty adolescent in a badly-tied tie in neon-orange company colours. Just you and the electric bulb you turned on for company but which is doing a poor job of illuminating the room, a room which is no longer oversaturated with sunlight and is starting to cling to the corners of your vision. The curtains behind which something might skitter, all limbs in the shadows. No one introduces prospective buyers to these things any more than to the spiders in the cupboards or the sparrows nesting in the eaves. Still, I'd want to know who I was going to be living with – wouldn't you?

Anyway, this is kind of just a long way of saying that I didn't get to see the new place before we moved. Wasn't invited along to a viewing at any time of the day. Just had to find out for myself what the shadows were like when we moved in. Modern place. Boxy little thing. Three bedrooms, two bathrooms, walls too thin for passageways. Not even in the dark.

So, you can see why I needed to get out of the house a bit?

Actually, the museum job is great. Very atmospheric, lots of new stuff to learn.

Like, okay, here's a weird one. All tetrapods started off with five-digit appendages on the end of each of their four limbs. Over time some of us might have lost a few of them, or even all of them, but all mammals are essentially walking around on the same feet, the same hands. See? I have five fingers on each hand, five toes on each foot. Beneath our skin, our hair, our fur, we are all the same animal.

***

Got that particular titbit from the constantly running voiceovers. Delivered eight hours a day in carefully modulated tones for maximum efficiency of delivery, specifically selected for the calming and authoritative timbre of their voices. Free to repeat the script every time the button is pressed.

Button jockeys.

They all swear it's a difficult job. Keeping your pitch even so you sound the same every time. Not tripping over your words when some idiot mashes the button and forces you to start again, and again. Not falling asleep in the quiet periods when everyone is crammed into the café instead. Yadda yadda yadda. What, you thought they recorded all those voices?

My job is a touch less... repetitive. Requires an imaginative touch. I sit inside the neanderthal diorama, right at the back – where the papier-mâché walls are flaking and you can see how the grumpy looking caveman's wig is a bit skew-wiff. Yeah, there. I sit in the shadows and re-pose the models between groups. It's real tricky work. You can't change things too much, too obviously. There aren't enough variations to get through a day like that. Just a shifted weight, a carefully turned head. Enough to freak the kids out when they come racing back from the sabre-tooth tiger two exhibits up, whining at their parents to hurry up and look at this one. Just enough to unnerve. Enough to make you wonder, maybe I just didn't remember properly? Three figures with glassy, unseeing eyes and tacky, stiff limbs. Purposefully unlifelike. And a fourth figure at the back, posed away from the viewer, almost entirely in shadow and just as still as the others but almost breathing with life. Like if you had a torch you would be able to see a real alive thing crouched in that diorama with them.

Proper creative stuff. Not everyone can do it.

It doesn't pay particularly well, but you make sacrifices when you find a job you really love. I had a friend who became a school teacher, she said exactly the same thing. The highest paid person here is the café manager, but that's just because that job is a nightmare to fill. Super-high staff turnover. The last one just disappeared mid-shift; got immortalised as an early European settler on the floor below – in memoriam. It's all a lot more sophisticated than the stuff I used to do at home anyway.

Quite often I'll go to the café at the end of my shift and hang out there for a bit. Technically I'm not really supposed to, but I got co-opted by the caretaker once as a spare pair of hands and I kind of enjoy it. Something to do with faulty wiring? All I know is they are forever having to replace the lightbulbs in there and he needed someone to hold the ladder while the bulbs slowly fizzled out one by one around us. Someone who wouldn't mind the dark. Rookie error really, it's the electric lights which make it so hard to see what's lurking in the shadows. But whenever the darkness is creeping in, I like to go and hold the screwdrivers while the caretaker mutters to himself and the waitstaff all huddle together around the glow of the till. It's professional courtesy really.

Generally, I don't leave till after the streetlamps are lit, which suits me fine. The new place doesn't have the weird floorboard with the screaming face in it, or the marks next to the kitchen door showing everyone's heights, or the thick under-floor carpet of fur belonging to a long-departed pet – but there's still room for me, just. It was a bit of a near thing, the old bedframe nearly got replaced with a divan at one point. I mean, a divan? Come on, that's just rude. No space at all under one of those. Stuck with a classic frame in the end though.

That first night, something else, some other resident inherited with the house, took the opportunity to climb onto the bed where the youngest was sleeping – trap them there paralysed and terrified. Muscle in on my turf. But it left a long, bare limb dangling over the edge of the bed. Outside the blankets. And, well, I soon put a stop to that. We won't be seeing that one again. It might not be quite as sophisticated as my day-job but there's still artistry in this stuff. Professional pride.

Besides, we grew up together – it's the least I could do.

Ilex

Distressingly manicured as the woods hereabouts have become over the past several centuries, for the most part there is little undergrowth to speak of. In order to make the cut – or rather, to avoid it – certain aesthetic qualities and nostalgic associations can be a boon to plant life. The last remaining genus of the Aquifoliaceae – the rest of the family long gone, whittled down through the ages – has made a go of it: the English variety, having been described by Linnaeus, is favoured by card manufacturers and birds alike, the latter feeding on drupes, their droppings dripping seeds across the forest floor, ensuring the continuation of the species. How many creatures, two or four-legged, with digestive tracts less suited to the particular cocktail of acids in those bright little berries, have spent feverish nights curled in on themselves, guts writhing, have perhaps perished? And yet the leaves of its South American cousin, when brewed, keep half a continent chipper and alert, causing harm to neither human nor beast. Maté, chimarrão, or cimarrón, regardless of which name appears on the calling card, has been dried and crumbled and ground and steeped and sipped since long before Columbus stumbled ashore, while the variety rooted on this little island way up north has remained prickly and unpalatable. Such are the vagaries of evolution, the whimsies of descent and modification.

In the sodden winter landscape, rife with murky mud and fetid foliage and bare branches, a sprig or two of evergreen cannot go amiss. It warms the cockles of our hearts, brightening the verges on otherwise colourless, squishy slogs over marshy fields and down slick woodland tracks. But the sprigs spring up into swathes, growing as tall as they do wide, spiny shiny barricades sprawling across the earth, intermingling with their fellows, tangling up the public footpaths, snagging wool from passing sheep, mercilessly choking out the tentative attempts of other plant life to stretch roots down into the soil and leaves up toward the sun. The English species, *Ilex aquifolium,* shipped across the sea to be commercially introduced to the New World, has spread there to such an extent – a rampant colonising force of glossy green torsed foliage – that it has been put on the list of undesirables. Condemned as an invasive species, no number of beribboned holiday wreaths can compensate the West Coast of North America for the inching, incremental loss of biodiversity.

That such a plant should come to be associated with the season during which it outshines its denuded neighbours is not unexpected, nor is the fact that it has become imbued with sacred significance by several sects: its contrasting colours and characteristic endurance lend themselves readily to representation and interpretation, inviting immortality in songs sung by minstrels, its prickly form sketched and etched on endless tidings of good cheer, year after year. Strange, though, that the properties used to tie it to that most pervasive of religions, Christianity, are so clearly linked to the final suffering of their saviour rather than to the joyous miracle of his birth. Emerald spiked leaves supposedly recall a thorned crown, crimson berries drops of blood. The constancy of colour is meant to remind us of eternal life. Yet it would be fair to say that the vast majority of us, when we festoon our doors and mantelpieces with carefully-arranged cuttings at the darkest, dreariest point of the year, are perhaps more inclined to turn our thoughts with somewhat hedonistic anticipation to mulled wine, mince pies, lie-ins, gifts and gatherings and general merriment than we are to dwell on the hereafter.

As far as the holly and I are concerned, this is perfectly acceptable. Brought low from the generous geographic range it enjoyed during the Cretaceous and having survived only as a relict on the fringes during the mass extinctions of the Late Pleistocene, *Ilex* is gloriously indifferent to any meaning that may be attached to it by such a novel species as Homo sapiens. The genus simply continues as it has done for the past several geologic eras: to hold its ground on every continent in one form or another, encroaching steadily through dioecious reproduction, the pollen passed from the male plants to the sterile stamen of the females. A warming earth may threaten some of its species, but *Ilex* are legion. In Europe, the lone representative of the clan remains robust and widespread, unchecked and unchallenged but for the annual trims for festive trimmings.

And so, the time being right for some prudent and unobserved pruning, I don my boots, armed with scissors and a carrier bag, and make for the forest, intent on surreptitiously clipping a few boughs with which to deck my halls.

Northfield from the Other Side

One hot, muggy summer – and there really isn't any other kind in southern Minnesota – I sublet an apartment in the small town where I was attending college. The Scriver building, previously the First National Bank of Northfield, was now home to the local Historical Society. The gift shop sold trinkets related to the building's notorious past: it was the location of the last, bloody raid of the Jesse James Gang. Two locals were shot during the attempt to rob the bank, and two members of the gang were then gunned down when the citizens of Northfield armed themselves and struck back. Things have been much calmer since 1876, but a street festival is still held every September to celebrate Northfield's homegrown courage and brief spell in the limelight.

Upstairs in the Scriver building, there were two or three apartments – all were quite spartan, and mine was oddly renovated (I had to crouch in the shower). Upon moving in, I did notice that a small crucifix had been pounded into the wood of the door to the common hallway, just below the doorknob, and painted over many times with glossy brown paint. I didn't think much of it – there are religious types everywhere, even in a town whose motto is "Cows, Colleges, and Contentment".

I settled in as well as I could, given that my furniture consisted of an air mattress and an old oak door spanning two milk crates to make a table. Not quite twenty-one and living on my own for the first time, I was unfazed by the inconvenience of my living arrangements, which sometimes veered into the absurd – such as the day I returned from work to discover that an entire Dixieland jazz band was set up on my doorstep, meaning I had to sit through the concert before I could go indoors. Another quirk was the kitchen cupboards: they had magnetic catches, but one appeared to be defective. It would click shut with a satisfying snap, but when I went back into the kitchen later, the cupboard door would often, but not always, be open again.

On a couple of occasions, friends who had stopped by to sit on the floor and drink wine while playing whist – forming a living tableau of the pretentiousness of youth – told me that the place gave them the creeps.

Of course, everyone knew the building's gruesome history – you could buy mortuary portraits of the deceased gang members, Clell Miller and Bill Stiles, on postcards in the shop downstairs. But this seemed to me a voluntary frisson, a fanciful association between the rather drab fabric of the historic building and the dramatic events of 1876. Stubbornly averse to superstition, I paid their remarks no mind and embraced my awkward new semi-bohemian lifestyle.

But then came the glasses and the crashes.

As students do, I occasionally left unwashed dishes in the sink overnight. One morning I woke to discover that the rim of one of the smudged, flea-market wine glasses had come detached, as though it had been sliced clean off and then carefully placed back on top. I pitched it and washed the others, assuming that it was a production flaw. A week or two later, I went into the kitchen only to discover that another glass had shattered, its stem left standing and shards scattered everywhere. This I did find odd because again, there was no apparent cause. Still, cheap glassware – I moved on with my life and resolved to tidy up more promptly.

Despite the fact that my air mattress had a slow leak and had to be pumped up again every night, I slept well and deep at the start. However, after a few weeks, I was woken up in the middle of the night by an almighty racket from the kitchen. I thought the wall cupboards must have come down, smashing their contents to smithereens, or perhaps the microwave had spontaneously exploded (it was a holdover from the 1980s and I had never fully trusted it). I flicked on the lights to discover that nothing at all had happened – not a thing out of place, except the usual cupboard door hanging open. I returned to my makeshift bed but felt uneasy, finding it difficult to settle my nerves.

After this happened several more times, I was forced to admit that something felt well and truly off. It became increasingly difficult to dismiss the history of the place out of hand: my mind's eye was drawn back involuntarily to the waxy, unseeing faces on postcards displayed on racks downstairs, sold for fifty cents apiece. I found myself wondering whether the two bullet-ridden locals had also been photographed, or whether that particular brand of sensationalism was applied only to the corpses of outlaws. Some nights I was all but sure that I could make out the vague outline of a figure, and would find someone actually standing in the kitchen when I switched the light on. It was only ever the cupboard door ajar. One night as I found myself poised next to the light switch once again, waiting less than patiently for my adrenaline levels to drop, I decided it might be an idea to simply stop shutting the cupboard in the first place. Scepticism is well and good, but being jolted from a deep sleep with a heart-thudding crash was wearing thin.

I never heard another peep from the kitchen, my wine glasses stayed intact, and the hairs on the back of my neck remained undisturbed for a month or so.

The day before I was due to move out in late August, I awoke to the sound of my alarm and rolled off of my semi-deflated mattress. Not fully alert, I pulled back the curtains and stared blearily at the spots in front of my eyes. Not spots – bats. Two bats had crawled in through a minuscule hole in the outer window frame and suspended themselves, heads down, snugly between the screen and the glass of the sash window. At first I thought they were dead and was rehearsing an awkward phone call with animal control, but then I saw that they were fidgeting – whether because of my presence or simply because it was getting lighter out, I couldn't say. Moments later, as if on cue, they began in unison to claw their way down towards one corner to make their exit. I didn't see them fly away.

It is beyond silly to think that the ghost of a slain local hero or infamous bank robber would turn poltergeist simply in order to nag a college student about domestic chores, or arrange a bat farewell. Coincidences account for much of what the superstitious would attribute to unsettled spirits.

But those bats….

My Husband's Mother

At four fifty a.m., I wake up but do not open my eyes for another minute, hoping to wake up in a different room somehow, in a different country, with different people. Just not this one. Just not here. Just not with them. When I was a new bride, I was asked to wake up every day at five, without fail, to begin by cleaning the kitchen floor, doing the laundry, and then bathing myself, only in that order. Then I was to sit in front of Lord Shiva's picture for ten minutes, to pray for the safety and wellbeing of my husband and my new family. That was so I could start cooking for the family of six, including my husband, his parents and his two brothers, with a pure heart and a pure floor, and be done with everything by seven, when the rest of the household would wake up.

I set my alarm for five a.m. right after two days of living in this house. No, it wasn't a house at all. It was just one square room with a small kitchen attached to it, the size of roughly two rows of four chairs each, tightly placed next to each other. Touch-screen devices didn't exist then. You had to press the asterisk at the bottom-left corner of the dial pad on your phone to go left and the hash to go right. I long-pressed '0' to open the menu, the down arrow button on top of the dial pad to go down to where it said 'alarm' on the dimly lit screen, and then I clicked the down button several other times until it went from twelve to five. I was still learning to use this phone that my father gifted me on my wedding day. He'd have hoped I would call him perhaps, to ask about his health, and how he was doing, or to confirm when it was okay for him to come see me. I was his only child, after all.

My mother passed away during childbirth, so my father let his brother, childless uncle and aunt, raise me as their very own. Aunty loved me like I imagined a mother would love her own child. She braided my hair every day before school, taught me how to read Urdu, and prepared an extravagant meal for all my friends on my birthday each year. Uncle taught me science and math, helped me with my homework and even bought the prettiest floral dresses for me from all his tours to other cities.

And then I turned twenty-two and my father decided it was best for me to get married. That's when my life changed. I never knew what it was like to have a mother, neither did I ever have that desire to need that knowledge before. But I have a feeling that if she were around, she would never have let my father get me married so early. She would have resisted, asked for some more time. Or at least, she would have prepared me for how ruthless and unforgiving married life was going to be.

I woke up at five for the first week. My small mobile, about the size of my palm, would vibrate each morning, loud enough for everyone in the room to hear. For the first three days, my husband's mother would grunt when she heard the loud vibration in the morning, and I would immediately turn it off. No one else in the house noticed the disturbance, it was just her. I would get up in an instant and go directly to the kitchen to start with the floor. I wouldn't wake up with the first vibration on some days. On those days, she would yell my name in frustration and wake the whole household up to let everyone know that I wasn't up at five. On those days, she would yell at me for every little thing throughout the day, as if to teach me a lesson for being so irresponsible. This happened for another couple of days. I would wake up with the first vibration on most days, but some days when my body felt too tired to feel anything, let alone the vibrating mobile, the screams of an old frustrated woman would do the job.

The room was extremely small, a single bed covered more than half the space available for the six of us. My husband's parents slept on the single bed, the two brothers right beside the bed, on the floor, followed by my husband, and then there was some space left for me by the wooden door that separated the kitchen and the room. One night, in my sleep, I felt a huge blow on my back, as if someone had hit me, punched me, right above my hips. It woke me up in an instant. The room was too dark for me to completely get a hold of the situation, with just a small lantern giving me a sense of location, dimly lit, placed over a small piece of marble on top of the bed, almost as a shelf, as big as a man's face. I was still where I had slept last night, and I felt the shadow of someone leaving the room. I hastily traced my finger on the dial pad of my mobile to reach the asterisk on the bottom left. I long-pressed it to turn on the little torch attached to the top of the screen. I pointed the torch to the family that was still fast asleep, to figure out which one of them had just gone out. It was my husband's mother. I pressed another button to light up the small screen on the mobile, to check the time, and it was three a.m. My husband's mother had woken up and gone out at three a.m.

I panicked for a moment, not knowing what to do. I was trying to think straight when I heard her footsteps again; she was coming back. I immediately lay back down, turned the torch off and pretended to be asleep. She came back, and stopped in front of my unmoving, languid body. She did not move for another second, and then she kicked my stomach, which was now facing the door, and then crossed over my body, to the other side to reach back to her bed. My gut scrunched in pain, but I held my breath, not letting her know I was wide awake. I let out a huge sigh when she collapsed back beside her husband.

She had just gone to the society bathroom, about ten metres from our house. It was her who had kicked me in the back before because I was in her way, sleeping in front of the door. She had kicked me again, in my gut, for the same reason. She could have just crossed over my body, but she chose to kick me, to cause me pain. Could I say anything to her about it? No. I knew if I ever even talked back to her, she would not say anything to me, but she would go to my father and humiliate him and my family. I know my father would feel ashamed, and I know he would not talk back either. The more I thought about it, the more helpless and violated I felt. I would cry on most nights, and my husband, who slept so close to me that I could feel his breath on my neck, would not even flinch at the sight. He took me to the kitchen on nights when he wanted to fuck me, but he would never ask me why I cried.

Eventually, my husband's mother started kicking me each morning when I would not wake up with the first vibration. By the third day of being kicked in the back, right above my hips, I learnt to wake up at four fifty instead. On my own. My body would just wake me, maybe because it did start anticipating the kicks, one after the other.

At four fifty, I wake up but do not open my eyes for another minute, hoping to somehow wake up in a different room, in a different country, with different people. Just not this one. Just not here. Just not with them.

Without Translation

The month, in the most part, had been a long one in which the only refuge had been hibernation, deep within the house. The children loved this all too well, tucked up on the sofa with mugs of steaming hot cocoa. The days melted into one another like evanescent watercolours, each one inspiring an energy within me.

I sat for hours at the desk in the library, my shoulders aching in tension, my eyes watching the clouds conceal the daytime through the window. A clock in the corner chimed on the hour but in truth, my time had never been governed by such precision. It was not particularly unusual for me to write ten thousand words in one sitting by the light of a dying candle, but more often than not, I would stare at the page as if willing it to speak to me, only to look up to see that the hour was starlit, and to realise that the children would be asleep on the sofa in the adjacent room, unfed and unwashed.

The children had always lived here but it had been a different place when their father had been alive. He had invited guests almost every day and people had passed in and out of the rooms, endlessly talking. Now we only really use a few of the rooms and the others lie waiting for something, under shrouds of dust, lost in repressed nostalgia.

"Can you hear us?"

The children opened the door and stepped hesitantly into the library. For a moment, just a very brief moment, I saw them as they were once, careless and untouched by modernity, holding their father's hands, distracted. He was a remarkably tall man but always, when he was with them, he would kneel, so that they did not look up to him but directly at his face instead. It always seemed to me that his eyes registered a sort of portentousness, as if he was already walking out of the door, years before he did.

I shook my head slowly, clutching the pen like an IV of ink, and walked towards the door, gesturing for the children to leave the room with the nib, my arrow of irrefutable destination. What I felt then was the loneliness and the presence of the Waste Land before me, the old-fashioned white of the page without the mind-synced clatter of the typewriter. I made a mark in the snow which was, in its essence, intrusive and incongruous, almost like the doodle of a crow.

Hours later, embittered by the page, it was the wall I was staring at when the letters first appeared: fine black calligraphic strokes on peeling grey paint. I hesitated, knowing that my sight had been deteriorating for some time – surely all I saw was a trick of the light, but as I stared, fixatedly, the letters began to dance in spirals and in curls across the wall and out into the hall. I followed them, as if they would lead me somewhere, but they just kept looping back, always to the library, as if they were owned there. Words were formed but sense was absent in these long and winding sentences, each one pinned in place by commas that did little more than erase the origin from which we had come.

I closed my eyes and for a moment there was a stillness, almost heavenly. Then I felt the clammy touch of a child's hand in my own. I could not bear to open my eyes but within seconds light invaded them.

"Can you hear us? It's not working. Can you help us?"

"Turn them off."

"And on again?"

They stood before me, larger than memory, phones in their hands and the cacophony of stranger's voices penetrating through pods in their ears. A sigh was my only response, and then they left me, though I could still feel their sweat on my palms.

I may have slept after that, in the library. In fact, I recall the descent of black ink, dark, like a widow's veil upon me, on a velvet winter's night. With little idea of how many hours had passed and a page before me, that was slightly wet, though I did not know why, I reoriented myself so that my back faced the clock.

Like apparitions they stood before me, phones in their hands, small figures judging me with eyes as vacant as dolls. With the pen sculpting my fingers, I glanced at them and said nothing, for they were watching me with terrible eyes, and their screens flickered hurriedly, almost anxiously, as if trying to display much more than time would allow.

"Can you help us?"

"I need to see."

My fingers fell upon the wall, though I could not remember standing up, and I felt the slightly raised lines on the paper where the ink had seeped in. It was real.

Without removing my eyes from the walls, I heard the children step towards me, their lights flickering to the rhythm of what can only be described as incessant and infuriating buzzing and pinging. I shook my head, closing my eyes and my ears to all their distractions; it was a world for them in which I had no place, not that I knew my place within the beauty of fiction either. All I knew was that the words were like a labyrinth through which I had to stumble, blind in my own silence, unwilling to hold those damp hands that tugged at my jumper, unwilling to gaze on those Medusa eyes that demanded too much.

"Leave me."

"Why are you looking at the wall Mummy?"

"I'm trying to read the words, but they keep – "

"Where are the words Mummy?"

"On the wall."

"Where?"

They were evidently trying to fool me; I was sure, quite sure, that it must have been the children who wrote on the wall, in such neat and winding spirals of forgotten handwriting, because it could not possibly, well hardly possibly, have been anyone else.

"Why did you do it?"

"We've only been on YouTube for an hour Mummy. You said – "

"But it's been a whole month since we began."

I turned back to the wall, ignoring their red lights, and stared at the words which were overlapping like ivy. It was impossible to ascertain any meaning at all from the looping black letters, but I continued to stare, transfixed, heart in my throat, until all I could make out was a jumble of letters. Excitedly, I rearranged them, quite sure that this was an anagram I could solve, but the answer I retrieved was a sentence so alien to my tongue that it must have been there, buried within, all along.

you are my riddle

That was when I knew for certain that these were not the words of the children at all, but something darker and much more sinister, something that could even be described as possessive. Slowly, the letters began to detach themselves from the wall and slide towards me, inching closer by the second like spiders. They wove a web around me and I could feel their touch so vividly, almost sensually, though I could not hear or see a single thing. The curled descent of the letter Y crept higher, caressed my collar bones and entwined itself around my neck, like a talon gripping me.

The phone began to ring and the children rushed through with their insistent lights and their mindless clatter.

"Can you help us?"

"The words – "

They stood silent for a moment, their eyes locked in confusion.

"Okay, fine, you can't see them! But just imagine – just imagine words on the walls, words falling from the walls, words weaving round like, like – "

"We cannot imagine."

I felt the blood drain from my own face in that moment and I knew that I stared on strangers.

"But you are children! Throughout time, throughout history, in books, in fiction, children have always had the gift of imagination, not yet cursed by the mundanity of maturity. It's as if you're not children anymore!"

The phone rang again.

"Can you hear – "

"Yes, I can hear it," I snapped impatiently.

For a moment they looked at me and their eyes were not so terrible at all, but then they glazed over and their screens started to dance again. I remember quite clearly that I stood, unable to move, watching them as they sealed themselves in that algorithmic existence, that destiny created for them, in that real world that was nothing more than illusion. I stood, as if a galaxy apart from them, reading words that played a part terribly indistinguishable from life. It was impossible to breathe with the words in my – on my throat, and with the pen burying itself in my palm, breaking the skin with its pulse, shedding blood on carpets of a long abandoned white.

The black rope on my neck led me, not out from the maze, but into the library where I stole a book from the shelf and turned its empty pages, unwilling to believe. Then I took another and another and another; they were all the same – vacuums of white, as if the whole history of writing had been erased. It was then that I dropped my pen in the wax from the candle, and saw, with unbound eyes, the red ink splattered on the Waste Land before me.

… and the child lay screaming unheard.

Wake-Steed

Before I became the dragon wreathed in oak-skin, a sire of reavers and blood-blessed thieves, and deliverer of terror upon fertile shores; I was the giant of a black forest. I was a yawn in the dark, letting small creatures pick for scraps between my parts whilst breathing life into the wilderness.

I let things eat at me, and rut in me, and rot in me. In a crucible of primordial contest, beasts battled for a sliver of the immortality I enjoyed. I outlived all their fang-studded maws slavering for devourment. I shed the things about me that were ready to die and let them drift as burnt-orange leaves down to a muddy grave; but I remained. White tusks of spider silk dangled between my limbs, and were torn away when the storms arrived.

I sank into my sturdy trunk, whilst chaos killed the weakest creatures around me, I dreamt. A shadow swept across the root-tangled earth, spear-charged, and fixed one flaming eye upon my boughs. He begged to swing beneath them in a noose. I told him to wait until the sky's panting settled. The grey shadow laughed and said that he would ask the ash instead, who was just as wise. I watched him depart with his spear dragging a canyon through the wet earth, and knew the ash would give him what he asked for, but he would never learn the oak's patience.

The roaring tree-breaker dwindled in its assault, and displaced birds returned with ruffled feathers to their nests. Rain felt like sex. Our spider-webbed roots, interlaced and overlapping, all nursed on the same sodden earth. We gorged on dampness and dead things. A nearby stump glistened in its veil of morning dew, and I counted its rings, sombrely ruminating. Two centuries had passed. I recalled a girl who led warriors to this place in the dim blue haze of dawn, and pointed a tattooed finger towards my root-kin. She was wrapped in an ox hide with braided hair as golden as sap, fastened by a bronze pin. The men in her wake took axes to the oak, and I wished a slow death upon that girl.

My insides scurried with reincarnations. Small things were born and rotted to dust in the same bark-wrought throne, and my mind wandered to strange realms of the imagination. I fantasised that small, strong men might come to release me from my woodland shackles; and in the minds of ancient forest-lords, inebriated by the wisdom of death befalling all things around us, fantasy often sired prophecy.

Appropriation

Torfey was staring out of her kitchen window with a reindeer skin draped across her naked shoulders, and a black cigarette dangling from her mouth. There was a pen in her hand and paper beneath it, but no art was coming out. She'd been commissioned that morning by the left-leaning Baldr's Party to sketch a banner for their campaign, reimagining their magnificent city as the bustling Norse trading centre it had been a thousand years ago.

Nothing in the city would have betrayed such a past to any outsider; It was as though Drevdagen's architects had given the project of constructing a real life 'Valhalla' to the makers of neon Chinese street food signs. Torfey's eyes skimmed the horizon desperately for any source of inspiration.

The most famous building in Drevdagen was within her sight, but she felt contempt at the church's fakery and preposterous size. Yrsaskirkje's curved black steeple emerged from the snow-laden fog like the prow of a phantom ship. It cut the same magnificent silhouette as a medieval stave church from Northern Europe, but where its ancestors rose tall on timber framing, Yrsaskirkje's tiered, overhanging roofs gleamed darkly like black onyx. Snarling dragon heads loomed from the edges of each tier, dry ice rolling from their parted jaws and neon lights gently pulsed from their nostrils, teeth and eye sockets. The temple hosted intricately carved portals decorated with interweaving motifs of beasts, some garnished with animatronics that made their limbs writhe and electronic eyes glow in the fading light. Whilst its exterior paid homage to the ancient, long-forgotten traditions of the soil it rose out of, the interior of Yrsaskirkje was the bastard child of multiple religions. There was nothing pious about it – the interbreeding of Christian pews, Hindu icons and Muslim ablution areas carried no spiritual weight.

Torfey turned her attention to the complex hologram shimmering overhead in pathetic mimicry of the aurora borealis, casting streets in an artificial green light. Huge, pixelated spectres of horned warriors astride wolves and bears flitted across the skyline. Hollywood-poisoned fetishes, wishing for what the past had really looked like; nothing more. Absent-mindedly, Torfey found herself sketching a crumbling city where holograms of leprous peasants and shuffling amputees plagued the night skies. She ripped the sheet out and tore it into tiny pieces before putting out her cigarette and going to the bathroom. She looked into the mirror and wiped some sweat from her tattooed face.

'A void grows within you and moans when you do not feed it,' the mushroom lady whispered from her seat in the bathtub. Her gaze was black and burned into the mirror. Torfey averted her eyes from the grey, mottled face and unlocked her phone. She turned up the brightness on her tattoos and adjusted the saturation until runes glowed phosphorous blue across her cheeks and forehead. The inked serpent coiling around her throat pulsed with a subtle pale light.

'Pretty,' said the mushroom lady, raising a long finger to point at Torfey's shoulder. The skin over the fingertip had burst into a drooping black tendril, 'missed a spot, sweetheart.'

'I know, I know,' the young woman hissed, turning to snap the shower curtain shut. Torfey was only angry because her mother had died some time ago, and conversations like these left her reeling for the rest of the day. Weeds had taken up residence in the bathroom's corners, and thawing snow dripped through the rafters infrequently; but otherwise, it had gone quiet.

Torfey knew about tourists, and she knew they liked you to fit the stereotype. That's what drove her to open the cupboard above her sink and rifle through its contents before turning her eyes from amber to ice-chip blue with two drips from a suspect pipette. She happily played along with the basics of the game, but would not overstretch her boundaries or engage in puppet dances for rich morons. Weren't they pioneers once? Masters of ship and sail, of art and culture.

'Raiders, rapers. Masters of war and death,' the black tendril began to reach around the shower curtain, and Torfey glared at it until it retreated.

If she really cared for all that crap, she would let her white-blonde hair grow out, but she insisted on dying it black. She tore through the knots with a hot comb and mulled on this. It felt deliciously anonymous to walk the streets of Drevdagen untouched by the stares or comments of total strangers. Her manager would have something to say about it, of course.

She would give the same excuse as always, she decided; she was of Sámi blood (true), her people were always known for being dark-haired (not so true) and that matching her hair to her high cheekbones may in fact present an unexplored side of Scandinavian history that tourists would feel intrigued by (she prayed to Fenrir that they would never feel intrigued).

It gave her the peculiar appearance of a thick build-up of dandruff in her parting, where really it was the paleness sprouting through that made foreigners slaver like dogs and pull expensive cameras from their bags. They had enough toys to ogle at without her pandering to their fetishisms.

She squeezed some blackheads out of her forehead and checked her body for mushrooms, and felt much better.

In the Morning

It was one of those cold mornings which winter sometimes gives you; the kind where the sun is so bright, it seems to sparkle in the air, as if it were refracting through glass. I had my jacket zipped up to the top, my scarf wrapped so tight that I could feel myself swallow against it and my breath was white like powdered chalk. Standing just outside the Orleston's house, I looked out over the park on the other side of the road. It was frosted over and sloped down towards the brook at the far end. There was a steady stream of cars going past.

Mr and Mrs Orleston had come to see me off. Rosie stood with them; still in her pyjamas with a hoodie thrown round her, shivering.

"You have to come over and stay again soon," Mrs Orleston said, hugging me tightly. "It's been so lovely having you here."

"No, please. Thank you for dinner and... everything else."

"Don't be silly," she said, waving her hand. "We love having you here."

Mrs Orleston had short blonde hair, large framed glasses and one of those smiles which told you that what was most important in her life was making sure everyone else was happy and comfortable. Mr Orleston, a large man, evidently an ex-rugby player, gave me a firm handshake.

"You take care mate. Come again soon." I thanked him, gave Rosie a hug, and started my walk to the station.

I had one of those peculiar feelings where you feel like life is one long, wonderful story and that you're playing a part in it. Hearing birds singing and dogs barking; stopping every minute to get a look at the sun shining on the trees, it was in moments like that where you wondered how there was ever a time when you didn't think life was wonderful and rich with possibility.

I played over the events of the previous night. I'd sat at the table, nervous, mildly scared of the dad and a little embarrassed in front of the mother. It didn't take long for this to ease. They fed me full of wine and all the food I could eat, to the point where I had to prove to them I was full, something Mrs Orleston refused to believe. Rosie's brother and sister were there too along with her uncle.

The brother sat at the end of the table, opposite Mr Orleston, in a subconscious attempt (I presume) to challenge him. This sounds spiteful, but I actually found it very funny. He had this arrogance which was so in your face and obvious, that it became a source of enjoyment more than anything else. Rosie's sister acted like she'd already known me for years. That is to say, she teased me incessantly in that way that only friends can, where the insults are no different to the kind children might use.

The uncle saw himself as an intellectual. He spoke about politics as if the people involved were personal acquaintances of his. If somebody brought up an opinion, he had always read "an article" which apparently disproved the position. And yet, like with his nephew, I couldn't hate his pretence. If you pushed him further and further on some argument he held, he'd eventually buckle and burst out laughing. This laugh was so contagious that you forget whatever it was you were talking about in the first place.

And of course, there was Rosie Orleston herself. You can't describe people like Rosie; it's impossible to say all they do for you and you cannot imagine your life without them. Even though I had only known Rosie for three or four months, I felt I had known her my entire life. She had told me so much about her family that when I actually saw them, it all felt more like a memory than anything else. I almost felt a nostalgia for these people, as if I had shared a long history with them already.

"What do you want to do after uni?" Mr Orleston asked me.

"Oh, I'm... I'm not sure yet."

"He wants to be a writer,' Rosie said quickly, then retreated into herself like a child does when they blurt out a secret.

"A writer?" the uncle said, as if he were weighing up his verdict as to whether or not it was a viable career. "What do you write?"

I never knew how to answer this question.

"I write short stories."

"About what?"

This question was even harder.

"I'm not really sure how to describe it. I like to write about real situations that happen in people's lives. I'm more interested in characters than stories. There's probably a name for this genre, but I don't know what it is. Anyway, I've just started."

"He's very good," Rosie said, in the same quick, sharp way she had before. I laughed awkwardly. "She's only read one of them so she can't judge. I'm trying to get better." Rosie hit me under the table.

"Ah, a writer," the uncle said, leaning back into his chair. "You know what I always say about literature? Literature is a form of simulation. It's the closest humans can get to inhabiting another mind and seeing what life looks like from their perspective." What followed was an exposition of his philosophy of literature. Again, I acknowledged that if anyone else did this, I'd find it annoying, but I enjoyed listening to him. We all spoke about our favourite books, and this led on very quickly to conversations about our lives. Conversations about literature usually follow this pattern. The conversation which struck me was Mr Orleston telling us about how he met his wife. He'd met her at a job for which he was completely underqualified.

"I almost didn't apply, but for some reason, I went for it. I had nothing better to do with myself, I guess. I was scared, thinking I would be fired within a week, but now I've been working there twenty years. And of course, if I hadn't gone there, I wouldn't have met my wife." Mrs Orleston blushed and I felt a surge in my chest, I'm not sure why.

"I think about that almost every day," he went on. "How different my life would have been if I had just let myself be scared."

After dinner, we drank wine and played cards. None of the adults in my family ever joined in with games like this. All the while, I kept thinking about Mr Orleston's story, about stepping into life and not being scared. I thought about all the time I had spent idly dreaming my life away and resolved that from tomorrow, I would live differently and that my life would truly start. We played for hours. At one point, when I went to get another drink, Rosie pulled me aside.

"Why didn't you tell them you were a writer?"

"I was embarrassed. It makes you sound pretentious"

She squeezed my hand. "Be proud of it."

I now pressed that same part of my hand, as I walked to the station. It was a reminder to leave my old life behind and live life differently. All of this might sound ordinary: a simple dinner round my friend's house, and yet, it felt like a turning point in my life. This was a normal Sunday evening for them, but I felt my life had changed. I saw something in that simple dinner, something which promised a life different to the one I had now. Couldn't I *be* something? Couldn't I *do* something? Who knows what this something was, but ridiculous as it sounds, I felt that morning, walking along a suburban street, my teeth chattering, my eyes blinded, that life was meaningful and had a purpose.

I got on the train and tried to read, but I couldn't focus. Vague images of the future swum around in my mind. I saw the city rolling past. Even when my view consisted of nothing but houses, apartment blocks and innocuous industrial estates – it still felt like they all represented a life seething with possibility. I had a romantic vision of throwing myself into my writing. Rising early in the morning, writing for hours, going to work in some café or bookshop while my ideas ran away with themselves in the background, then returning home to continue writing. It would be tough, but why should I let that scare me? What else did I really want from life?

I got off at my stop and made my way home. The sun still shone. The air was still made of glass. As I got closer to my house, I wondered what I could do to start this new life of mine. I didn't know what I would do, but I felt a passionate yearning to start something. I'd step through my door into a new life. I got in and the first thing I heard was the TV blaring loudly in the living room. I went into the kitchen where my mum had just finished making herself some coffee.

"Hello. Did you have a nice time?" she asked.

"I had a great time actually, I-"

"Hang on, hang on," she said. Her phone rang, and she had to take the call. I went into the living room and said hello to my dad. I started trying to tell him about the other night, but he was checking his messages while I was speaking.

"You're not listening, are you?" I asked.

"I am, I am," he insisted, but he carried on as before, giving generic one-word answers. Not only did I feel awkward, but I felt stupid for trying to tell him about something I considered to be meaningful. It felt almost like tossing around a sacred ornament: it could break easily and ought to be treated with a certain level of reverence. Eventually I gave up and went upstairs. Both of my brothers were fast asleep, and I didn't see them till the late afternoon. I spent most of the day trying to read but couldn't. Reading now felt like a waste of time. I looked around my room. It was strewn with clothes; the shelves were covered in a film of dust. Was this where I was supposed to be writing? Is this where I would start my journey?

Later on, I went for a walk, but again, it felt pointless. My surroundings were just as pretty, just as aesthetic as they were that morning, but it was as if the life blood had been drained from them. I remembered my walk from the Orleston's house, how I had stopped to look at a tree – how pathetic was that?

At dinner, we didn't sit at the table. Everyone was balancing their plates on their laps. No one spoke to each other. The TV was showing a programme which no one was interested in. I tried to start a conversation, but every attempt died within a minute. My brothers were scrolling on their phones while they ate. Was this the same life as last night? Did both those places really exist together? Now all my dreams of living felt completely out of reach. I could no longer see them. I looked at my family and couldn't help resenting them. Why? Why did everything change in the space of a few hours?

As I lay on my bed that night, I let all the impressions of the past couple days run over me. The Orleston's house... the boasting brother... the teasing sister... the arrogant uncle... Rosie touching my hand.... And then I thought of what I had just seen: my dad's apathy... my brothers' laziness... the monotonous, banal life which seemed to eat away at my passion, like a parasite. How could I start living? When would I start living? What was the first step? I thought of the Orleston's again. Maybe they were playing a game right now? The brother was probably boasting about winning. Perhaps the uncle thought he was going to win but ended up losing. Mrs Orleston probably didn't understand the rules. Mr Orleston was probably better than he gave himself credit for. Rosie was probably laughing...

Floating in Sweven: An Autobiography

These things of purple descend. They horde my mind. Blemish me. What was once white and black is revealed to not be colour at all. Just tone. Varying in their darkness and light to sway what is refracted into my eyes. If these are eyes. If what I perceive is what is real, or just my perception of sensory information. My brain defining, relating, interpreting. Finding patterns in chaos. Something in nothingness. Meaning where no such convenience is possible.

It cannot, then, this perception, be called reality. The state of things as they actually exist. Who decides, by their discernment, what is the state of things? Humans, birds, lizards?

The mantis shrimp, whose sixteen colour cones rival our three. They see in ultraviolet, infrared, polarized light. They see more than any other being on our tiny planet. Shouldn't that make them the supreme decider of what is real?

Perhaps. Perhaps mantis shrimp are too big to see reality in its closeness. Live too briefly to appreciate its length.

Tardigrades, piglets of moss, bears of the water. Small and sturdy. They are seemingly designed for the endless voids of space. Therefore, they possess this appreciation. Or at least, that is how I personify their existence. Maybe I am wrong about the nature of them. Maybe they, in their eight-legged plumpness, simply relish the joys of swimming. To be submerged. Floating in a semi-solid. Drifting. It was something I once appreciated, before it was taken from me. Twisting fates. Shades of time. Cursed figure of flesh made living by this nervous system. A jellyfish on a frame of bone. My body forsaking my mind, and in its abandon, the mind fails.

Am I then, distorted in my selfhood, able to, see?

Can I, in my state of change, of growth and of loss, know what it is to be.

Am I even a candidate to perceive life, haunted by a dream of childhood. Day and night, a wish for this flesh to stop its systems of biological magic. For the muscles to become stiff. The heart un-pumping. Eyes clouded. Bowels emptied out in the easing. To be freed from a world I never gave permission to be admitted into. Return to the place I was before my birth. To nothing. A nothing I cannot even comprehend. For us humans, to imagine nothing is something.

What do I have now? Touched as I am. Tainted in the grip. Broken by force. My life thrown back to shore over and over again. Driftwood in the endless tide. Pulling and pushing at my smoothed fibres. Cells swollen and burst open. Bleeding out into my stiffening joints and useless limbs.

In reality, I once had some health, and that is my curse. I have changed for the worse and those who knew 'me' before cannot accept what I have become. Is their view, an outside perspective, the true way of the world? They want me to fight against circumstance. Positivity will mend the corrupted codes of my DNA. A good attitude would turn these stairs into a ramp. If I smile and nod long enough, will they eventually stop 'helping'?

Yet, when I am mournful - as I should be, because there should be no happiness in this - I am accused of laziness. Pathetic creature. Luxuriating in self-pity.

So, I embrace it. Claim pleasure in my new life. Just for a moment...

J'accuse!

'So, you're a benefit leech then?' A liar. Why else would you enjoy being like this? Scum. Rat. Thief. Undeserving, regardless.

LEAVE ME ALONE.

'So be it.'

And thus, it started. My isolation. Two years in, the world joined me. And they mourned. And they complained.

How can we live like this? Trapped in our homes?

Maybe this is where my perception of reality is useful, experienced as I am with imprisonment. Stuck in a wheelchair upstairs, with no safe way to descend. Entombed in one and a half rooms. Afraid that if I try to leave, my body will betray me. The world will judge me, because I am too young to be this way. Too young to have given up a fight that could have never been fought.

'Thanks, I'll let my chronic illnesses know.'

But at least I have these colours that have come, bursting, into my tones. Not that anyone accepts them. I am married to a man; so how can I be 'the gay'. I revoked my place on the rainbow in the eyes of those who have never been there. Who have seen it only at a distance, rising from the storm. Fragile in the gloom, drawing on its strength from a burning ball of gas 151.05 million kilometres away; and from fragments of water vibrating together.

Must I accept the reality they see, to survive for as long as my failing body bears it? Not for me, though I wish deep in my heart that I wanted that. But for my husband, disabled by Autism and long Covid. Stressed to breaking by the task of keeping me alive. For my adopted children, who meow for my affection, purr by my head, kneading my belly. For the baby due Christmas Eve.

Blemished tone, touch, technicalities, circumstance and the horrors of operating human flesh. Drifting in my bed with night crawling into my room. Purple descends on me. Bruises from my past.

I am penetrated again. By memories. Recollections of wounds that long ago healed into thick scars. Yet, I still bleed. It soaks my sheets.

I exist inside a semi-solid state, swimming again, if only in my mind. Drowning by the hands that pull me under. I struggle beneath a broken surface. Destined for the deep.

Floating in Sweven.

Hostile Architecture

You are told to be present in your body. The seminar leader says he wants everyone to appreciate themselves, to celebrate the bodies we are in. Your camera is off, so he cannot see your expression, how you sink. Usually you turn your camera on, but today the thought of having to look at your own face is too much to bear. Onscreen, you are just a name and a set of pronouns that no-one knows how to use. You try to go along with the exercise, to do as you are told. It's like forcing your hand onto a hot pan. You recoil from yourself. You cannot be present. You cannot be here.

You go back in time, see yourself in the grey bones of Sarajevo, blasted and besieged. String up all the banners and balloons you like, it will still be a war zone. How are you supposed to celebrate a place that does not want you alive? How are you supposed to live where you are not wanted?

The seminar leader moves on, sets a writing prompt. He tells you to write two characters interacting through dance. You try, but you can't. You are still in Sarajevo. The siege lasted one thousand four hundred and twenty-five days. You have been alive for eight thousand one hundred and seventy. The average life expectancy for your country is eighty years. It is significantly lower for people like you. You do not want to die, but how are you supposed to survive? You are not wanted here.

You danced as a child, took classes for many years. You always got dressed in the bathrooms, never in the changing rooms with the other girls. You were exposed enough as it was, the skin-tight leotards and corpse-pale tights a poor defence from the eyes of others. Sometimes, when you danced, you would forget how you looked, living in the movements of your limbs. Sometimes, you were beautiful. Free.

But in every classroom, there were floor-length mirrors. Between dances, you would stare at yourself, fixating on the dips of your hips, the uneven swell of your breasts, the dull-eyed stare of your desolate face. You could never escape yourself. You never will.

Thankfully, you are not asked to read anything out loud. You are expected to work on the prompt after the session concludes, and send it off to the leader for feedback. You know already that you won't. You don't have it in you to dance. There will be no consequences, just a nagging sense of guilt, but guilt has always been a second home to you. You close Zoom down and spend the rest of the evening feeling sorry for yourself, only crawling into bed in the early morning.

When you dream, it is the same one you had that night you spent at your grandmother's, when you ran naked in the night to the bathroom, fast enough to keep from making a mess on the carpet, but not fast enough to get to the toilet, so you had to quietly clean blood and liquid shit off of yourself and the bathroom floor. In the dream, you are cut open, an incision made down the left of your abdomen, and you watch as the hands reach inside you and extract a giant tumour, smooth and pale as a pearl. There is no blood, only the glowing white of the thing that was inside you. You marvel at the flatness of your stomach, how simply you have been fixed. When you wake and feel the bloated stretch of your belly once again, your eyes sting with tears.

The doctor gave you pills for your stomach, but they have done nothing to help. You had a colonoscopy booked at the hospital, but they cancelled on you at the last minute. Short-staffed they said. You will have to wait two more months. Two more months of belly-stretched bloat, of bone-deep fatigue, of remaining housebound so you can dash to the toilet at a moment's notice, shitting blood and fearing what is happening inside you. You hope it's not cancer. It probably isn't. You don't know what it is. You won't know for at least two more months. You have to survive until then.

***

Sometimes, your eyebrows make you want to kill yourself. You are fully aware of how ridiculous that sounds. It does not change the despair that claws at you when you look in the mirror, see and feel the spider-leg strands protruding, sharp and insolent. They grow from your chin and cheeks too, fat black thorns bulging from your skin. You debate electrolysis or laser removal, but whichever you choose it will still be a years-long process, expensive and painful. Ideally, you would have your whole body stripped bare, rid yourself of the loathsome growths that plague you all over, but that would be thousands and thousands of pounds that you simply do not have. Thinking about it for too long is enough to send you into a spiral. So instead, you pluck and shave and squeeze your face raw, and shop for skirts that don't show so much as a sliver of ankle, so you can move without feeling the long hairs on your legs plucked and pulled with every movement. They do not help you be seen for what you are, but you could shave your head and wear nothing but cargo pants and muscle shirts with a bound chest for the rest of time and still would get called 'Miss', so you cannot bring yourself to bother. You like the floor-length swish of your skirts, take comfort from the way it makes you feel, how your body is hidden. Anything that brings you comfort is to be clung to like a life-raft. You pair long black skirts with bright red jumpers. Red is the colour of strength. You want to be strong. You are told you already are, by those who love you and those you have never met. You do not feel it. You just feel tired.

They teach you about the concept of autofiction on your course. You have mixed feelings. You know the liberation of putting your wounds down on paper, of ripping them from the festering dark and finally exposing them to the air. But the world has a vested interest in your misery, all too quick to commodify it: *roll up, roll up! Come see the latest addition to the cabinet of curiosities! Its parents were told the poor freak would never have the capacity for meaningful speech, and yet! It speaks! What a success story! A heart-warming tale, it's enough to make Herr Asperger shed a proud tear! Come now, lift your shirt, let them see your wounds! Yes Thomas, dig in there with your fingers! Don't squirm, how is he supposed to know your pain if you won't let him touch? What's that Thomas? You're curious as to what 'it' is? Is it a man or a woman? Let's find out! Come on now, don't struggle, spread those legs!*

You could expose every inch of yourself, turn yourself inside out until you are quivering viscera, and still never be understood the way you want to be. You have made peace with that. You no longer blame yourself for it the way you used to. It's the double empathy problem: when two people with vastly different experiences of the world come together and interact, they will struggle to understand and extend empathy towards one another, leading to misinterpretation and conflict. It's no one person's fault, it's just how it is. It's not the idea of not being understood that bothers you so. It's the thought of being consumed, treated not as an individual sharing a piece of themselves, but as a symbol of the marginalised experience, a synecdoche that magically grants the ability to breach that fundamental gulf of experience and empathy, granting complete comprehension of you and everyone like you. As if you were required reading, existing only for their edification, their understanding. Just the thought of it makes you want to slam your head into a wall – yours, or someone else's.

The last time you saw him, your father said you need to open up more. Never mind that every time you did, prying your ribs open to expose yourself to him, he would look away in disgust and tell you to clean up your mess. He called on your twentieth birthday, the one that began with you awake at midnight, tears streaming down your face as you wrote to your lecturer, trying to explain that you wouldn't be able to get your essay in on time due to how you couldn't get through a day without breaking down crying, due to how your family was breaking down, how your body, your mind, was breaking down. Your father called you later that day, and asked what you were working on. You looked at what you had written, about dashing his head in, his blood and brains spraying all over the rocks, and running far, far away, and said "oh, just stuff".

You haven't spoken to him in over two years now. You still have books left at his house. You want them back, but you would rather cut off your own leg and eat it raw than ever step foot in that place again. You don't regret cutting him off, but you wish you would stop seeing him every time you look in the mirror, wish he would stop showing up in your dreams. Sometimes he shouts at you, berates you. Sometimes you remain civil, tension boiling away under the surface, the way you did back when you were still poorly playing the part of the loyal daughter, planning your escape. Sometimes he bursts into tears. Those are the worst. You never wanted to hurt him. You just wanted him to stop hurting you.

***

That poem you were writing, when he called you on your twentieth birthday, you think that was something like autofiction. You poured yourself out onto the page, finally able to look at yourself spread bare, and put into words the things you had never allowed yourself to think. You are proud of what you wrote, but it hurts to look at. It takes you back to those days of coming apart at the seams, of locking yourself in your room and not sleeping, barely eating, just writing, the only thing that could bring you comfort. You are doing better these days. Not well, but better. You are not the person you were back then, trapped in a life that was not yours. You are doing your best to never be that person again.

You think if you were to write any autofiction in the future, you would not write as 'I', but 'You'. You like the idea of forcing the reader into your skin, into a world and life that does not fit them. You cannot tell them how it feels to be 'you', to explain yourself. But you can show them. You can force their face against the hot pan and, as they scream, hiss into their ear, "How does it feel? How does it feel to be me? Tell me, how does it feel?"

You will not allow voyeurs to your suffering. You have to be there. You have to feel it.

Last Round Birthday

When Sylvia wakes up, the only reason she feels compelled to leave her bed is to provide immediate relief to her hangover. Pickle juice has never, throughout the years, let her down, and as she drinks half of the jar. She tops it all off by crunching on the chunkiest pickle. However, instead of the relief after crunching down something cold and refreshing, the gelid centre of the pickle provokes her back teeth to a harsh protest and as she moves the slush in her mouth to the front. It squeezes through the gap where she expected her porcelain bridge to be, and falls to the ground. Perhaps she could have been more moderate with the wine and spirits last night, but it was Ted's seventieth birthday so why would she hold back? Nobody truly knows whether he will ever celebrate a round birthday again. Judging from his state, Sylvia fears he won't even make it to seventy-one, let alone a whole decade from today.

It may not be immediate, but alcohol takes its toll eventually. It has been a year since West died of liver failure. Everyone knew it was coming, but no one could, or perhaps dared to put a time on it in fear of accidentally cursing him; or worse, insulting his wife, Simone. Sylvia never truly liked her, but they nonetheless developed a friendship many years ago when their mutual interests of locating their alcoholic husbands night after night brought them together. To be completely honest, Sylvia only needed Simone to help her locate Ted, who was most definitely with Simone's husband. Simone, on the other hand, engaged in the rituals of typical female comradery; she discussed makeup and the prices of various unnecessarily flashy clothing items, and she would often end up modelling for Sylvia at night when getting hold of their husbands was impossible.

With Ted still asleep, it would be a good idea if Sylvia cleaned up a bit. Maybe that way Ted may fail to recollect the fiasco that took place the previous night. Not that Sylvia ever drank so responsibly as to remember anything at all, but considering her track record and the shattered windows in the apartment, she is certain she will be blamed for it. You created everything you hoped wouldn't happen on your husband's last round birthday, everyone would say. Her limbs feel oddly heavy and unresponsive as if she were moving through some weird dream and each time she picks up a glass from the floor, shattered or not, it retains the stench of last night's contents, which rushes Sylvia to the bathroom countless times before she manages to tidy the apartment. There is nothing she can do about the shattered windows.

***

Ted wakes as a result of a sharp stabbing pain originating from somewhere at the back of his head. It is so fierce, it forces his eyes shut with such immediacy, he doesn't have enough time to notice whether the sun is out, or even whether he has woken up in the daytime to begin with. It wouldn't come as a huge shock if he hasn't however, mainly because he has been waking up in the middle of the night with exceeding frequency since he lost the ability to walk. Alcohol takes its toll, Sylvia always says. Or something like that. If this is daytime, then where is the familiar plinking sound of plates being stacked and cutlery being compartmentalised? Isn't that what he normally hears when he wakes? Isn't that what he both admires and hates about Sylvia? Why do you cook so early? He always says, We don't have little kids anymore. Today however, Sylvia's usual murmur of productivity is replaced by resonant belching of her throwing up. Oh yes, it was my birthday, Ted remembers. Or was it?

Struggling to sit up, he yearns for the days when he could get out of bed, without a word leave the house, and not come back until Sylvia was fast asleep. West accompanied him on their daily escapades to the local bus station. They sometimes sang as means to afford cheap cherry wine, but they normally left that up to West's father, whose charm on young women is still unmatched. Life had been so much easier back then; he could walk to the bus station and be far enough from Sylvia during the day, but close enough to drag himself home at night.

There was a tall cherry tree with thick healthy foliage which shaded the blue bench on which he and West spent their days. West's father, who had married Sylvia's aunt, often joined the two men, under the unspoken understanding that the women's histrionic bitchiness simply ran in the family. Despite being significantly older, West's father projected an undoubtable charm with his powerful tenor notes and a vibrato that was too slow, which was often rewarded by young men and women. It was mainly West's father, remembers Ted, who culminated the money for cherry wine. Ted and West would sit back and watch the performance unravel. West's father always wore perfectly ironed trousers, cowboy boots and showed off his golden tooth off to the side, with a grin he learned from some old Western film.

On a particularly bountiful day, they could drink three to four two-litre bottles, and when the sun sank and it was time to go home, Ted always used to say that everything beautiful has to come to an end; a saying that has stuck with him to this day.

Today however, once he manages to sit up and open his eyes, it feels as though the beautiful thing – if you could call it that – which will soon come to an end may well be his life. There is a still damp patch of blood on his pillow, roughly the size of the back of his head. It is brown, ruddy, almost brick-coloured. The sight of it brings yet another more pronounced pang of pain to Ted's head, and this time, it feels so concentrated, he can locate the very spot from which it originates. It is on the left side of the back of his head, not quite behind his ear but thereabouts. When he touches the area, it immediately protests and causes Ted to hiss until the pain subsides.

"I'm going to your doctor's appointment," says Sylvia. It appears as though she says this more to the door as it closes behind her, than to him. But the message has nonetheless been conveyed. West's drops, which his doctor prescribed for the painful build-up of liquid in his knees, have throughout the years become a lucrative business. Certainly, pallid-faced addicts are willing to buy the thing for triple its original price to later manipulate it in some rather impressive chemical manner, and turn it into their preferred drug.

Although it's the middle of summer, it is cold before the sun comes out. If West could walk, he would close all the windows and perhaps even turn the heating on for an hour or two. To warm up quicker, he could also do with a drink to wash down the aftertaste of the Vodka he drank last night. It feels as though he drank it only a few minutes ago and with his eyes closed. Could that be possible? Yes, it is almost like an instinct; he can be sleeping or knocked out by Sylvia, and he would still be able to navigate perfectly in the murkiness to locate a bottle with precision. Anyway, most of the money goes to Sylvia because she says so, but she also gives him a small commission, which will buy alcohol for at least three days. Four if he drinks a bit slower, but then there are all those fevers and cramps and blood blisters...oh, it's a long story.

As he looks towards the windows, thinking he may be able to drag himself close enough to shut them since his bed is not situated at all far, he sees that they have been shattered. The shards that he sees sprinkled across the carpet however, wouldn't make up the whole of the missing area of glass, which means that the rest must have been sprayed outside onto the road. Ernest's body feels oddly light, as if he had lost half his weight overnight. Or could it be that his bed has this whole time been floating a meter above the ground, gently rocking left to right? Swooshing up and down?

"Did you ask for more than usual?" he asks Sylvia when she returns. The moment he heard her fumbling with the keys, his bed sank to the ground with a thud; so loud it is now stuck somewhere deep inside of his head. Agony. He can taste blood at the back of his throat. Now his stomach feels filled to the brim with shit and maybe if his body hadn't been so used to alcohol, he would have been able to throw up as a result. But it no longer functions in a self-protective manner, fighting to find and provide the most immediate relief to any injury or discomfort. Instead, it has become static. It drinks and it drinks more, then it sleeps and then it wakes. If he eats something bad, his body won't flush it out, nor will he throw up. Likewise, when he is unwell, his body doesn't sweat to rid itself of toxins. He will only experience these symptoms until he drinks them away into numbness. You could say alcohol is his form of pickle juice.

***

There is a peculiar comfort in drinking coffee from a glass. As Sylvia drinks it, she keeps an eye on the pot of chicken soup that simmers behind her. Finally, Ted is fully awake. Once again, he is bleeding, but Sylvia cannot conjure up a reason for it this time. It wouldn't be bold to assume he has attempted to stand up and walk after drinking so much he forgot he had lost the ability. It wouldn't be the first time. It strikes Sylvia that If she appears too eager by engaging in a conversation or offering to clean his wound, he might interpret it as her expression of guilt and blame her for the injury. At the same time, if she remains this still and unmoved, he may think she is preparing to launch another attack the moment he utters a word. Sylvia knows it wouldn't be the first time for that either.

She doubts Ted still loves her. Far from it, she would say. Instead, after the practicality of life replaced young love in their early twenties – someone had to help her with the new-born – nothing was ever the same again. Does she still love him? As her vision moves across the apartment, she notices Ted as he inhales the smell of the soup. She is aware however, that no matter how well it may turn out, he will not as much as look at it, let alone eat any of it. Sylvia hasn't seen him eat for a while.

"Food can get so boring after a while," he once told West, who couldn't disagree more.

"What women want is some bulk, to be thrown around a bit", he said, "and how will you do that if you eat like a fly and drink so much?" West may have sounded wise and all, but Ted still thinks he must have done something right, considering the fact West is now rotting in some damp deserted place, a good few feet underground. Ted can't pinpoint exactly what that something he has done rightly is though.

"Women love a good pounding, and you need a lot of strength for that, my friend, trust me" said West. As far as Ted is concerned, West had always been so crudely comfortable around his father. The assumption that Ted and Sylvia plodded through the rituals of sex only proved to Ted that West never listened. But if he told West any of this, he would only respond with shock and disbelief, which would infuriate Ted even further. But you're only in your forties, he would say. Or something else equally irritating and true as that.

Ted hated that side of West. It could have been the age gap, but that, if Ted remembers correctly, was very narrow. So, what was it about West that could at times make him so damn relatable?

Most certainly, it was the fact that just like Sylvia, Simone acted as though her husband was largely insignificant, and yet awaited his return from the bus station each and every night. The moment he would open the door, she would smack her lips and shut the bedroom door before him with a resolute bang. Unlike West, however, Ted often ended up with a tooth missing or a fractured nose on many of such nights, which his friends never got to find out. He would stay home for a week and do anything Sylvia demanded to be able to safely co-habit under one roof. When he recovered, he immediately returned to the bus station and life went on.

Rotation

I am an addict.

I inhale. The air is dirty.

The circle of strangers nod. One by one. Like toys with spring heads that jiggle. Too loose in the neck.

An encouraging smile from the woman in white.

She recants her prescription Bible – 'We understand. We understand. We understand.'

The room is musty. The coffee and biscuits taste bland. I am offered orange squash as a substitute.

"It's got just the right balance of concentrated juice and water."

My eyes roll back in my head.

I am an addict.

"Tell us more."

I was alw-

"But only if you feel comfortable."

I was always-

"This is a safe space."

I was always add-

"There is no pressure."

I was always addicted-

"Take your time."

I am trying to tell you-

"Take your time."

If you'd just listen-

"Take your time."

I am an addict.

"Same time tomorrow."

The session ends. The room ascends. The people pretend.

I exit out onto the street. Opposite is a bar. I cross the street. The cars avoid me. It is cold out. Snow drifts across. Like in winter. I like winter. Everyone is cold in winter.

The barman nods as I enter.

"The usual, is it?"

Not today.

"You sure?"

Yes.

I sit with my lime cordial. It is bitter. I miss ale.

The room chatters. The young flirt and laugh and cheer at the ease of
existence. The old remember what it was like to be young and flirt and laugh
and cheer. There are a million stories in this room. A million tales with
beginnings, middles and endings that will be forgotten when a better anecdote
arises. Or when the booze kicks in. Or when people are no longer interested.

I have a story.

He sits across the room. He looks at me. He is drunk. His head wobbles.
Too loose in the neck. Like those toys with spring heads that jiggle when
you whack them. But he looks at me. Right at me. Blue eyes. Sky blue.

Do you want to hear my story?

Our moment passes. He orders another round. I order a lime cordial. We
drink our delicacies apart. I talk to myself.

The final bell rings. I sit and wait. He puts on his velvet trench coat. He is
beautiful. He looks back at me. I say nothing and the moment is gone.

An encouraging smile from the barman in black.

"Same time tomorrow."

The session ends. The room ascends. The people pretend.

I am an addict.

I wake up. I put on a jumper. I look in the mirror. My reflection looks back. We nod at each other. My morning coffee is bitter. I miss my lime cordial. I add sugar. I wait for the moment to pass.

The circle is smaller today. Less people nodding. I make my own orange squash – no water. I listen to the millions of stories with beginnings, middles and ends. But the ends are always in this room. Every single time. Is a story worth remembering if we know where it ends? I am bored. So bored. I finish my plastic cup and crinkle the remains. Then I crush. Then I shred. Plastic does not decay. If humanity disappeared at this moment, the only memory of my existence will be this destruction. A monument to orange squash.

I inhale calmly. The air is bitter.

I hate being an addict.

"Tell us more."

I hate being here.

"But only if you feel comfortable."

I am not comfortable here.

"This is a safe space."

I want to scream.

"There is no pressure."

I want to be better.

"Take your time."

I was always addicted. This-

"Take your time."

I was always addicted. This is w-

"Take your time."

If you'd just fucking listen.

"Same time tomorrow."

The session ends. The room ascends. The people pretend.

I exit out onto the street. Opposite is a bar. I cross the street. The cars avoid me. Not the cars. The people in them. The snow is cold. I like the winter. Everyone is cold in the winter. Apart from when they have fires.

The barman nods as I enter.

"The usual, is it?"

Not today.

"You sure?'

No.

I sit with my pint of ale. It is bitter. I miss the coffee.

The room converses aggressively. I remember being young and flirting and laughing and cheering at how easy life is. Why would you ever want to be old? The million stories mix in the din. Mine is better. The booze kicks in. People will be interested.

I have a story.

He catches my gaze again. We are both drunk. Our heads wobble. Too loose in the neck. Like those toys with spring heads that jiggle when you whack them. Their plastic smiles unchanging even when a petulant child smacks their closed fist across their skull.

Do you want to hear my story?

Our eyes connect in the dimmed lights of the bar. His, blue water. Mine, red fire. No one should be cold in winter.

I was an addict.

We flirt and laugh and cheer at the ease of life. The snow melts. I refill my spirit. We drink together. Our moment lasts.

The final bell rings. I sit and wait. He puts his velvet trench coat on me. He is beautiful. He is so beautiful. He looks right at me. I say everything in this moment.

An encouraging smile from the barman in black.

"Same time tomorrow."

The session ends. The room ascends. The people pretend.

I was an addict.

I wake up. I put on his jumper. I look in his mirror. My reflection looks
back. I do not know this person. My morning drink is sharp. I miss my ale. I
add tonic. I wait for the moment to pass quickly. It avoids me.

The circle is just me today. Them and me. They want me to nod. Like a dog.
Too loose in the neck. Like those toys with spring heads that jiggle when
you whack them. Their plastic smiles unchanging even when a petulant
child smacks their closed fist across their skull just to see them wiggle up
and down like those toys with spring heads that jiggle. I alter my orange
squash so it has the perfect balance of concentrate and water. My eyes roll
back in my head. If humanity disappeared at this moment, I would be all
that is left. With my story. A story of flirting and laughing and cheering
because life is easy. It's what we all want. That story. It's what we all crave,
every day, in every moment of our lives.

We are all addicts.

"Tell us more."

I'm leaving.

"But only if you feel comfortable."

This is a bland substitute for existence.

"This is a safe space."

I want to *laugh*.

"There is no pressure."

I was always addicted. This is who I am.

"Take your time."

I was always addicted. This is who I am. This is who I wa-

"Take your time."

I was always addicted. This is who I am. This is who I want to be.

"Take your time."

IF YOU'D JUST FUCKING LISTEN.

"Same time tomorrow."

The session ends. The room ascends. The people in white pretend.

I throw my plastic monument aggressively to the side. I go to the bathroom. I inhale. The air is sweet now.

I exit out onto the street. Opposite is a bar. I cross the street. The world avoids me. The snow is warm. I love the winter. Everyone is cold in the winter. Apart from me. I am ascending.

The barman nods as I enter.

"The usual is it?"

Yes.

"You sure?"

Yes.

I sit with my buzz and stories. It is sour. I miss the plastic.

The room converses manically. Maybe this is the secret. Maybe this is the prescription Bible only worshipped by the few who believe. They understand. They understand. They understand. The beginning, middle and ending no longer hold a distinction. They swirl in the million stories of the room. The ease kicks in. People are scared of stories when they cannot predict the ending.

I have a story.

I am dizzy from the rotation. I catch him by his face. I am drunk. The blue water of his ocean eyes fills my sunken sockets. I look at the aqua-mirror. My reflection avoids me. He is cold. He is not interested. He has heard this all before. Again and again and again. My eyes rotate back in my head.

Don't you want to hear my story?

My spirits empty their guts out onto the snow-coloured tiles of the blindingly white bathroom. I want this moment to end. I want this moment to end. I want this moment to end.

I am not an addict.

The final bell rings. I lie and wait. A velvet trench coat disappears from the corner of my eye. I cry tears. I do not understand. I say nothing in this moment. Where is the surprise end?

An encouraging smile from the barman in black.

"Same time tomorrow."

The session ends. The room descends. The people have gone.

I am not an addict.

I am not an addict.

I am not an addict.

Up.
Mirror.
Reflection.
My morning is bruised. I miss my orange squash. The moment lasts till the end.

The circle is full today. Complete.

I want to be better.

"Take your time."

I want to be better.

"Take your time."

I want to be better.

"Take your time."

Do you want to hear my story?

"There is no pressure."

This is my story.

"Tell us more."

This is always my story.

"Let us begin."

I exhale. The air is clean.

I am an addict.

The Mycelium Myth

It had become a nightly ritual to eagerly listen to my father's stories of my mother. I would dive under the covers and, soon enough, the tales would commence. My father told me of the lands that they had travelled to together and how much they'd longed for a child of their own to tenderly love. I was told that my mother would pray every night for me. She would press her hands together and look up at the cascade of stars that adorned the night sky and beg for a child. But for every day that I did not come, my mother and father would weep a thousand tears.

In front of their cottage, a sapling had been planted many months before. As their longing for me grew, the plant grew and grew into a fully-fledged juniper tree. One harsh winter's day, after preparing supper, my mother went to pluck some juniper before she noticed several scarlet beads fall on to the pure white snow. She had cut her finger slicing an ambrosia apple, but the cold of the day had dulled her senses and she had scarcely noticed the wound until now. Standing under the tree, my mother had sighed, "how I long for a child as red as blood and as white as snow".

Three months passed; the snow had melted and given way for new life. The nearby fields were full of rapeseed to harvest for oil and newborn lambs who mewed for their mothers' milk. The forest became dense with budding trees; the earth had become a mass of roots intertwining themselves with one another. The scent of the juniper tree, now in full bloom, began to waft through the cottage. Overcome with joy, my mother plucked some berries and began to devour them, the juices dribbling down her chin as she did so. Her stomach shortly began to turn, and she recoiled in discomfort. "If I die," she told my father, "please bury me under this tree." A month later, I was born as white as snow and as red as blood. With her heart so full of joy, my mother passed on.

Whilst I slept in my crib made of beech and pine, my father buried her under the tree. Although I was only days old, I could remember feeling an emptiness and latent longing for my mother's touch, the warmth of her flesh.

When my father remarried, the stories came to an end. His new wife bore him a second daughter, Evelyn, whose skin was pearlescent and pink. As my

father was an alchemist, he had an acute sense of smell and would always
comment on how sweet my new sister smelt, like amber, honeysuckle, and a
fine spring day. My stepmother did not bestow the same kind of love she had
for her daughter to me. She cast me unforgiving glances and smaller portions.

As my sister grew, my father cast me to the shadows at my stepmother's
bidding. Whilst Evelyn was given fine foods; I was given morsels and
scraps, fit only for a dog. Naturally, it was to my great surprise when my
stepmother one day offered me an apple.

"Here we are, take your pick before Evelyn," she said, guiding me to a
large mahogany chest. It was in the depth and varnish of the grain, past the
engrained emblem of her family crest, that there was a slight morbid hue of
the slaves' blood-stained fingertips. She opened the chest, and inside were
three dozen or so emerald-coloured apples. I salivated as I could scarcely
remember the last time I had eaten well or had fresh fruit.

"Go on," she coaxed. "Take one."

I placed my head in the trunk, ready to pluck a delicious apple. And as I
bent over to do so, she crashed the lid, and my head came off cleanly with
one swift slice. It was then that my stepmother placed my head back on my
shoulders and began to sew it back on. Where my head had been severed
the flesh splayed. The sutures were so poorly done that the threads began
to snap that it would not be hard to see where the incision had been made
and the blood that was still seeping down my throat. And in my hand, my
stepmother placed an apple to make it appear as though I was taking a
moment's pause whilst enjoying the apple.

Evelyn, eager for the fruit herself, entered the room. "May I have an
apple, too?" she asked softly. I said nothing, for I was dead. Evelyn tried to
take the apple from my hand, which remained tightly clutched in my lifeless
fingers and gasped at the icy nature of my flesh.

"Mother, Mother! I asked Rosalind for an apple and she did not answer.
She is pale and cold, like a ghost!"

"Go to her once more, Evelyn," my stepmother said, "and if she does
not answer, clip her ear."

Evelyn returned to my body once more and asked for the apple once again. I remained silent, and so she cautiously tapped my ear. With that, the final stitch came undone, and my head rolled down the staircase, over the cobbled floor, before finally stopping next to my stepmother's feet and the boiling pot she was attentively stirred.

"What have you done?" she cried. "No one must know! But what is done cannot be undone; we must hide this." And so, she took my corpse and began to slice me ever finer until I could be placed in the boiling pot alongside the broth, vegetables, and herbs and the remains of flesh began to broil. Evelyn wept with such great sorrow that her tears fell into the pot too so there was no need for added salt to season.

When the stew was finally cooked through, my father came home and asked, "where is Rosalind?" My stepmother said nothing, Evelyn wept, and he ate ravenously. "Why are you weeping Evelyn?"

She said nothing. He began to devour the stew. If I had had lips or a tongue or a throat I would have cried out in pain. But he didn't notice, and after voraciously devouring the stew, he began to cast my bones to the floor. Evelyn began to carefully collect the remnants of me, gathering what she could and placing them into a handkerchief. Like my mother had before me, Evelyn took what was left of me and buried me under the juniper tree in the courtyard.

As the days went on, I began to decompose, and seep into the earth. I could no longer smell or taste or touch, but I could think and feel and hear. And then I heard the low hum of my mother's cries. Fine tendrils of her mycelia began to wrap themselves around me, and soon enough I could no longer sense where she ended, and where I began.

We had become a clustered haven of microbial forms; ephemeral yet eternal, skimming every surface like some rhizomatic parasite. And here is a handful of shadow we have brought back in a moment of truffled solace. The bulbous off-white heads catch droplets of rain as though an umbrella for tiny faerie folk who dart amongst the leafy autumn bedding. They make us think of better things, elven creatures and woodland nymphs and the possibility of life from every nook and cranny.

Soon enough, we could sense that the man I had once called my father had long forgotten about me. But it was Evelyn – who had grown and grown – who would solemnly kneel by the tree from time to time and weep.

It was one day, a year later, that stepmother had begun to pour through this sacred shrine. We imagined our taste upon her tongue; bitter, earthy, rich. And so, she one day plucked several of our crimson-spotted skulls. Our bodies were to be used in a pie for which she had spent the morning carefully preparing the pastry and herbs. She diced us, cut us, finely sliced us; it was just another part of our cycle for us.

And when the pie was ready, she and my father gorged on it. Flakes of pastry crumbed their mouths, filling smeared on their chins. It was then that their stomachs began to curdle, to recoil in horror at our poison slowly flooding their veins. Their eyes bulged and the two clasped at their throats, but it was too late.

When Evelyn saw their lifeless, putrid bodies, she knew what to do. She pushed the old, mahogany trunk downstairs, and placed them inside, contorting their limbs beyond the recognition of human shape.

This way, they would not be part of the great mycelium, under the juniper tree.

Profiling

The things I know about Caroline before we meet: she studies film at
university, she has no selfies with cat face filters but has professional-looking
DSLR shots instead. She asks in her profile for people to send her dog
pictures, so I send her one of my pug looking shiny-eyed in an elf hat. She
says you can tell a lot about a person by what dog they own. I text that I'm
not inbred and asthmatic, but I am pretty cute too. Since it seems to fit her
vibe, I ask if she owns a Golden Retriever. She's allergic.

We arrange to meet in a cafe in the student district. Walking there, I
recheck our conversation and realise that neither of us has explicitly used
the term date, and I'm anticipating meeting another straight woman who
bizarrely uses Tinder for making friends. The café opens onto a garden
with a large wooden pergola knotted with hanging planters, macrame and
string lights. Wood and sawdust stink sweetly under the sun. Caroline is
expressionless, staring through me before her eyes flash in recognition. A
wide compensating smile. She gets up to give me a polite hug and a nice-
to-meet-you, and her white milkmaid dress balloons in the wind. She says,
just checking, this is a date, right? Her voice is high and lilting, matching the
abundance of exclamation points and cutesy emojis she uses online. Her
pictures, even in high-definition, didn't do her justice.

Once we have dispatched the brief blurbs of our life so far—our
backwards hometowns, a staid discussion of A-levels, our favourite
guilty pleasure media—we get onto the customary coming out stories.
I consider myself lucky to receive disapproval from my grandparents at
worst. Caroline says her parents are reservedly accepting, but her mum is
adamant that every woman thinks that other women are naturally more
attractive than men. Caroline says, who's gonna tell her? Flat white foam
crowns her upper lip for longer than what is socially acceptable, but she
seems unbothered, which is perversely alluring. She explains how she's
writing her dissertation on Ingrid Bergman; I believe she's talking about
Ingmar Bergman and admit that I haven't seen much of his stuff, which, on
recollection, provides an involuntary cringing tic.

When our brunch arrives, she holds her phone in front of her, aiming at the food first and then panning slowly upwards to me. Caroline explains that she uses an app to film second long videos every day, and at the end of the year it will condense these clips together and speckle them with film grain – providing a shortcut to the brevity and texture of memory. I admire how she can confidently decide which part of the day to film and not hold off thinking something better is due. She's made me into a flash, subliminal, amongst this montage in the making. There is the sweet prospect of possibly winking in and out of more brunches, in front of seascapes and sunsets, and I imagine her taking shots of me running with hands spread wide in a field of purple wildflowers under Instagram-worthy golden-hour light—a slightly premature line of thought. Cool, I say, sorry, where did you say you were from again?

On the topic of exes, she brings up the impossibility of her last relationship working out: her ex was a stubborn Taurus, she is a fiery Aries, so understandably they kept butting heads. She asks, what's your placement? Responding with Sagittarius, I think that if I were a man she was dating, he probably would say something along the lines of, isn't Calgon a sign, or constellations are arbitrary and composed of random stars thousands of years apart. She says Aries and Sagittarius suns get along like a house on fire and asks if I know my moon and ascendant. Apparently, the confusion on my face is enough for her to send me off with the name of an app that can show my full astrological chart. All I need is my birth date (down to the minute) and birth location (down to the hospital location).

Needing to text my mom for the details extinguishes some of the spontaneous element to the romance. In response, she warns me to be careful as scammers have gotten smarter and not to give out any personal information online. She links an AOL.com news page concerning identity theft and the dark web. She only relents when I throw her a bone and reveal this is for an astrology site, and there's a girl involved. The details are in a baby book she has with my medical records and graphs that diligently track each roll of puppy fat, stuffed to the brim with accompanying bug-eyed baby pictures. This book and I, plus any date I brought to the house, are intimately acquainted. Killing the mood, my mom describes jaundice that made me look like a new-born alien and how I was born breach. Ass first, she says, tell the girl that explains everything she needs to know about you.

The app shows me alchemical looking symbols for what zodiac sign each planetary body was passing through at the exact moment of my birth. There are eleven columns with signs for each planet that can be in a further eleven different houses. A visual representation refuses to clear anything up, as it looks like a dreamcatcher. Some planets stay in constellations for decades; Pluto was in Sagittarius when I was born, which means I am part of a free-spirited and optimistic generation. The app's notifications seem set to replicate a text from some friend who is a bottle of wine deep, spliced with a new age, crystal toting therapist for milfs in California. One notification reads, 'Instead of seeking external validation from romantic interests, find that deep within yourself' and another states, 'You talk about other people because you lack a stable sense of self-perception.' Ouch. What happened to the generic Cosmo mag predictions of money trouble or unexpected conflict?

The next time we arrange to meet, we agree on an evening date at a place of her choosing. Spin Cycle is a faux laundrette, and inside too many chrome surfaces gleam under the fluorescence and self-satisfied signage commands 'wash it down' and 'come in clean, leave dirty' in a cursive font. I think, oh god, am I going to have to drink from fabric softener bottles ironically? To my relief, the bar behind the facade doesn't take the kitsch that far, and it boasts the same aesthetic as most other speakeasies: exposed brick, velvet chairs, warm lighting set flickering as low as possible, unthreatening bartenders in suspenders and bowties. Usually, people I've dated, who've taken me to these passworded places, acted like it's an exclusive secret, when they have simply found the weekly code on the bar's Facebook—they aren't going to make it hard because they literally want your money. Luckily, Caroline seems self-aware and says, I know it's a bit much, but I promise the drinks are delicious.

My legs are off-colour in tights and glittering under the low-light. Squeezed in spanx, tights webbing me at the crotch, I have hiked knee-high boots on and sausage-skinned myself further into a vinyl miniskirt. The plasticky fabric creaks and snarls its upper lip to curl over at my mid-thigh; I'm grateful that Caroline doesn't hear or acknowledge the noises. Armed with my new knowledge of signs, my sun (Capricorn) moon (Pisces) ascendant (Virgo), I am ready to seem open to spirituality and attuned to myself. I say, to flex that I have done my homework, that I have two earth signs and one water sign, and is that unbalanced? She responds, do you know your Myers Briggs? Luckily, I do, and I mention how my workplace had an initiative where we took the test to adapt office practices to our personality types—ground-breaking changes that lasted all of two weeks. I am introverted (I think, but who can be sure?), intuitive, thinking, judging. Without digressing, she says that makes a lot of sense. When pushed, she says a lot of words like practical, dependable, and grounded: synonyms for boring. She says, you probably keep a diary to organise and make sense of the day, don't you. She really has me there.

An overpriced cocktail arrives in a ceramic fish pitcher—the style of fish you would find on the tattooed bicep of a sailor—which comes with a side helping of a cherry red fortune fish. Hold your hand out, Caroline says, and shuffles closer in her seat to cup my hand with her delicate fingers. She watches the fish spasm. According to the list on the packet, a moving head and tail indicate that a person is in love. The possibility that this is what my fish concludes, or the fact she's so close, has me holding my breath as if any sudden movement would have her skittering away. Then the fish becomes a curled ouroboros, and she picks it up from my palm and wiggles it like she's hooked it. It means you're passionate, she laughs. I tell her he's my wingman.

In Caroline's defence, the drinks are delicious, and mine tastes pretentious but good: something akin to smoked apple juice. As we drink, she pulls out her notes app on her phone and shows me a long list of names: Anna (ESFP/S:Leo, M:Cancer, A:Virgo/Sanguine), Rachel (INFJ/S:Aquarius, M:Pisces, A:Taurus/Melancholic) and so forth. There are at least 30 names. With my tongue, I pick at the decorative shavings of gold leaf that have clumped and wedged into my back molars like cavity fillings, hoping this is not visible in my cheeks. As she scrolls down, I feel decidedly less special knowing she might have asked other people the same questions. I'm confused about the list's use; does she use it to consult the accuracy of their placements whenever people exhibit behaviours that deviate, or is it a *gotta catch them all* situation? I ask, are these exes? Absolutely not, she says, and navigates to where I am on the list to make an input.

Caroline walks me to the train station for the last train home. We are talking about Brad Pitt, but I think we are really filling the gap with nothing serious before we get to the awkward loftiness of saying goodbye. When we kiss, she fumbles and bites hard with a canine, like our first kiss is her first kiss proper. I imagine Caroline is more nervous than she lets on. I tell her that dentists shave those teeth down for the aesthetic back home in the States, and I grin to show my filed teeth. She says gross without a second thought. Laughing, I announce that on that note, I'll go.

The next morning Caroline checks in to say that she had a great time. I take another personality test, this time of my own volition, but mainly so I can strike up another conversation. The four humours test states that I am melancholic, meaning I have an excess of black bile, which gives me the attributes 'cold and dry'. It would all feel very Shakespearean if it wasn't for test questions such as: would you consider yourself a party animal? I send a screenshot to Caroline, who replies she is sanguine, the draining-blood-with-leeches one, and her attributes are 'hot and moist'. She adds a winky face for effect.

I wait for Caroline to initiate another date as we text on and off by sending astrology memes the other will find amusing. She adds me to her Instagram, so I consciously try to leave an appropriate gap before viewing her story. Caroline has started a postgraduate degree and is now a proud cat-mom to a hairless cat that won't set off her allergies. If I were an asshole, I would respond and say that no cat is one hundred percent hypoallergenic because the allergen is in their saliva, not in their fur. Our texts are getting further and further apart. I think about bumping into her everywhere—like brushing hands with hers while grasping at the last plant-based bacon on the shelf at Tesco.

By September, we haven't texted in months, but I feel like I still know her intimately from seeing her life documented online. Caroline posts a spare room advert which asks for a housemate with a cardinal star sign over a mutable sign; she wants a roomie who fits the household's independent atmosphere, rather than someone with an emotional-energy-draining placement. I think, what a load of shit, and unfollow her.

POETRY

Folk Material

I woke up in the museum
gift-shop – after taking a nap
in a stained bean-bag –

I felt as threadbare as its
nylon casing –

while the whitish specks
of its neat stuffing – like perennial snow
or breadcrumbs, scattered

all over the ground.

My tired hand rested
on an infographic –

where centuries were counted
in mattresses of ice –

twenty of them had fallen since

the needle was left behind.

Small and wooden,
it seemed to speak
in dropped tongues, and tallied stitches –

in the shrill pitch
of a splinter weaving –

through ever-thinning ice:

exposing the scarcity of preservation –

clothes fashioned for their own destruction –
fishing nets tangled into extinction –

the needle-shaped impression – already
fading from my fingertips.

morning after

a butter yellow
itches the window,
as stencilled sunlight
prickles the pillow –

morning dregs,
through eucalypt spittle –

and coarse paper cereal
sticks to the teeth,
as ear-ringing yawns
turn crisp on the lips

of a wine-glass with dust-scabs
that begs for drink –

on the tacky floor tile,
with caustic cold water,
where straw-legged spiders
and clod of conditioner

make fleeting quickstep
on the base of the shower –

a wire coat-hanger
in aerial twist,
catches a song

and the roof-groove sings –

shrill with the cackle
of thrilled kookaburra –

through the morning plays
a tin-can sonata.

Virgin female

a single fly,
from black static bottled –
is drawn out with the long
          pinch of forceps –

and held in the glare
of microscope light –
as her ruddy shoulders
          are rubbed raw white –

the air stiffens between her wings –
          crisp in the branches
as silver birch sails –
that reveal her bristles
          in fretful flickers –

each flinch as fine
          as infant whiskers –

and in the folds of her lantern legs –
          suspended with some vacant poise –

a belly rounded –
          soft and ripe
          with sticky cactus fruit.

Atoms of Sound

May be fused
or defused.

Or refuse to elucidate
their lucid state
as they feel the sharp
touch of nightmare
break them,
as they feel the flat
touch of dreamscape
wake them,
as they listen
to choirs of angels
blind to the Bible
forgetting the voice of prayer,
of tongues,
even of the Rosetta Stone:
sylph-like
riddling sphinxes.

A sentence splinters
a word wanders
a syllable checks the clock
a letter crashes –
only sometimes
in the Hadron Collider.

A clock ticks –
glass burns the fly
and you're back
with your feet on the ground,
with your hands on the table,
with your eyes on the page:
all numb
atoms of sound –
defused.

Scissors in air

I seem to be sinking,
      deep thick dark thinking,
            caught in a place.

                                    A door opens (
                                       somewhere

                    – Scissors in air –
Cutting
            tearing
                  breaking
all apart

They are coming...
--drawn
by the flute
                                rising over
                      /
              /
/
                  a spinning land
repeating itself
                                    over
over
                                    over
over

I seem to be sinking,
      digging tunnels/ mines deep in time
          caught in the mind
which reminds,   reminds,   reminds

they sit _ and stare
and don't know it's

                                                there,

here,

--everywhere--
reflected

                                               refracted

in fr   ac   ti   on   s

A tongue peals away from the roof of the mouth
like a metronome
metres and metres from   home.

Reimagined
in paint,
in pain,
words falling like rain.

                       Stalactites in caves

where I wander - - - - - - - - - - - - - -
on and on - - - - and on and on,
and water drips
       down
             and down
                     here.

They come
             to trickle in
like animals in the arc
two by two
four by four
day by day
year by year
again and again and
they all hear the sound of the flute
<u>her voice above it all</u>

                                    You will listen

The land slides

                    and it's broken)

Blóðsögur

I treated the world like it had ripped you from me
and raged, and raged
but in the seat of my soul I knew
that you still roamed this realm
one-eyed, hooded and spear-wielding
rearranging stars and destinies
for your amusement
it was the myth-weaving that I held dear
that was what you took from me

My tongue lay mute for years
the mead of poetry withheld.
I died of starvation many times.
Lost were the verse, and the metre,
the kenning, and the joy of spilling out
darkness before it poisoned me.

Thank you for my blindness,
o father of primordial song.
Wise were you to make an enemy of wolves
or maybe you couldn't understand
their wailing poetry; the privilege
of the moon alone.

A tapestry of sinews;
warped nightmares, wefted stories,
half-formed, nascent in the dark of my throat
I spat them out, vitriolic curses on you
for bestowing such a gift and
tearing it away, when I needed it most
the wilderness howled and guffawed
it told me to have faith in my fury

'I am hurting' I shrieked into its thorn-barbed maw
'Yes, and you are creating' it smiled back

These are my offerings to you.
Blood-sagas; cell-woven
bone-hewn, whispers in the vein

With every word I bleed
I grow more powerful
I bleed gods and cities into the black earth churned,
gorges sliced asunder by weary swords
dragged on their journey home,
sulking in their blood-drunk fullers
at the death of their glory days
no more would their thirst be sated
no more would they taste the soul of man
suffocated in its scabbard,
singing to their masters in the night:

'Better I grow soft and yielding in the furnace
than hung up; a corpse, the relic
of a war-hero grown frail,
honour's-bane trembling his flesh
at noises in the dark.
Kinder to return me to some molten state
rebirth me as a fire poker, some farming tool,
I beg, let me not rust and decay
trapped in the shape of something divine
once drenched in bloody honour
or take me up and let me cleave again
again, I beg, everything again.'

The House on Bentwood Road

Door of the forbidden
Typical, really
An average haunted house
Varnish sagged grey-brown
Peeling and shedding
Door knob may have shined, once
Now stained and blotched
No reflection
Not 'gold-like'
Speckled and rough
The knocker
Touch-creaking
The door opened
Into a dark hallway

Broken-in
Chipped paint
Rasping wrecked wood
Nearly gutted
By the elements
In shadows
With spiders
And possums
Were stories
Of demon cats
Using sharp teeth
And claws
Eating their way out
Of our stomachs
Writing maggots
Pawing entrails

In that corner
Another story
The Bentwood Witch
Indoor-lynched
Crimes against man
Dangerous to extradite
Hanging from every rafter
White toes above him

He climbs
Second floor awaits
Loud wood announces
His pitiful ascent
It's getting colder
He arrives
Legendary room
The place she died

Veil-like curtain
More than little
Riddled with holes
In slight breeze
Casting spotted shade
Over corpse-bed
Now a nest
For something with fur

It was so cold
Chestly pins and needles
Numb fingers

Shivers of recognition
Flashes of fresh linen
And new polish
He reels
Backing away
From unreality
Sun arriving at night
In the window
A figure appeared
Heavy dress
Mud and twigs
Embedded
On her clothes
In her hair
Inside her eyes

There's blood
Blotchy
Thick-trickling
From a spot
Between her legs
Soaking through
To the surface
Purple neck
Torn fabric
Fragmented corset
Set into her flesh
Mouth broken and blue
Nails missing
On outstretched hand

In a blink - closer
Shhhhhhhhh
Hissed through brown teeth
Pressing a finger
Against his lips
She was inside him
Her mind trapped
Every second of her death
Scream-scratch
Tear stains against sheets
Begging for death
His hands on her throat
Begging for life
The pressure
In their heads
They can't breathe
Please stop
He begs
She can't
Trapped
Unable
Please
Help

They find him
Two weeks later
Forever inside
The house on Bentwood Road

AUTHOR BIOS
in alphabetical order

nv baker

nv baker hails from the United States. Originally from California, he considers the southern Rocky Mountains his home. nv baker is a summa cum laude graduate of UC Denver and is currently enrolled in Durham University's Creative Writing MA program in the UK. When he isn't writing, you can find him considering what it means to be stymied between the imagined and the rendered. His work is in *Fence, RHINO Poetry, Prelude, The Crab Creek Review, Juked, Hobart, Ruminate, The Fourth River, J Journal, NYU's Black Renaissance Noire, High Desert Journal, The Roanoke Review,* and other publications. nbakerv@gmail.com - twitter.com/nv_baker

Aimee Dickinson

Aimee Dickinson is a master's student at Durham University studying English and Creative Writing. She enjoys writing short stories, plays and radio dramas, and has been on the writing team for the audio drama 'The Three Musketeers' and the Durham Student Theatre shows 'Away' and 'Foundations'. This is the first time Aimee's work has been published in an anthology and she is incredibly excited and honoured for others to read her scribblings.

Imogen Dobson

Imogen Dobson is studying Twentieth and Twenty-First Century Literary Studies. She is from Nottingham and completed her undergraduate degree in English at the University of York. Imogen loves reading: her favourite novels are J.M. Coetzee's *Disgrace* and James Joyce's *Dubliners*. Her MA dissertation will focus on female sex workers and their relation to the city in contemporary literature. She hopes to eventually do a PhD and publish a fiction novel.

Matilda Forrest

Matilda Forrest is currently studying for an MA in Twentieth and Twenty-First Century Literary Studies at the University of Durham. She is also in the process of writing a murder mystery novel in her spare time.

Sierra Kaag

Sierra Kaag was born in Bavaria and raised in the northwestern United States. She studied Art History at Carleton College in Minnesota, Art Conservation in Florence, and Art Museum and Gallery Studies and Creative Writing in the United Kingdom. With a keen interest in history and the personal and cultural significance of objects, her fiction and creative nonfiction explore themes of belonging, the experience of place, and the outdoors. Her writing is informed by the years she spent working in museums and cultural institutions in the United States, Germany, and the United Kingdom.

Megha Kaul

Megha Kaul is an MA Creative Writing student at Durham University. Having prepared for engineering exams all her life, choosing a Bachelor's degree in Literature and then a Master's in the same seemed like the most obvious choice to her. She is from Jammu and Kashmir in India, and feels extremely passionate about the history of her homeland. Her writing is significantly influenced by the experiences of her parents as migrants, experiences of the domestic, the indoors. Apart from being a literature student, she also enjoys dancing through all her troubles.

Nora Kelly

Nora Kelly is a biology-turned-literature student, who is currently studying for
an MA in Literary Studies at Durham University. In 2019 she was awarded
First Place in the Honi Soit Writing Competition in the Non-Fiction category,
and is working on diversifying her portfolio to include poetry and other
creative forms of writing.

Amber Natalie Kennedy

Amber Natalie Kennedy is an English poet and fiction writer currently
studying for an MA in Creative Writing. She holds a BA in English Literature
and is also the Co-founder and Editor-in-Chief of Spellbinder quarterly literary
and art magazine. Amber enjoys promoting literary communities and has been
the president of both her school and university creative writing groups. She
has self-published a volume of poetry, *Immersion,* and a novella, *The Remains
of Beauty.* Her work also appears in *Better Than Starbucks* magazine as well as
Write Now Lit, and is forthcoming in the *Ice Lolly Review.* Her most recent novel,
Prison House, explores themes which are prominent throughout her prose,
including architecture, isolation, addiction, fame and obsession.

Sofie Kitts

Sofie Kitts is a writer and Viking history enthusiast based in York, England.
She is a lover of mythology, particularly that of Northern Europe and
the art of skaldic poetry that flourished in medieval Iceland. During her
undergraduate degree in Scandinavian Studies at UCL, she spent a year
studying in Oslo, and grew increasingly drawn to the complex metaphors
and beauty of the Norse sagas. She also incorporates themes of Nordic noir
and dystopias into her writing. She has just self-published her first book: an
illustrated collection of dark fantasy tales and skaldic poems inspired by Norse
and Anglo-Saxon literature.

AM Mac Habee

AM Mac Habee is an award-winning artist and published author born in Montreal, Canada who is currently living and studying in England's North East. They have a particular interest in multimedia, interdisciplinary and mixed forms that break with tradition. As a non-binary, pansexual and disabled person, their work will often challenge issues of inclusivity, contain strong diversity themes or tackle emotions associated with being part of minority communities. In the two pieces of this anthology, AM interacts with the theme of 'The Great Indoors' through semi-surrealist and horror-poetry writing styles, mirroring the interiority of a mind in isolation. Twitter @artinginteralia

Hardev Matharoo

Hardev Matharoo is a short story writer whose work explores how different individuals respond to and make sense of the world. His narratives are character-driven, usually exploring themes of love, disillusionment, creativity and the search for meaning in one's life. With a focus on realism, his work attempts to portray the different facets of life as we actually experience them, with an emphasis on acute psychological description and emotional exploration.

Lua Morgenstern

Lua Morgenstern, a lesbian of indeterminate gender, holds an endless love for all things horror and noir, and chooses to explore themes of isolation, abjectness, and monstrous existence in their writing. They like to play with set notions of form and genre, and centre the experiences of the disabled and queer within hostile worlds. Among their influences are the works of Franz Kafka, Sarah Kane, David Lynch, and Seosamh Lily. They grew up in Northumbria, but recently relocated to Plymouth, where the seagulls are even larger and more aggressive.

Ladislav Pecha

Ladislav Pecha's interest lies in the ageing and decline of love: whether depicting a couple whose forty-year-old marriage has reached a plateau or two inexperienced teenage lovers who once thought they would spend their whole lives together, time, love, and ageing dominate his writing. One such short story has been featured in a creative writing anthology in the past and Ladislav hopes to one day share his work with larger audiences. In his literary studies, he is in the field of medieval romance with a particular interest in the conventions of courtly love and chivalry.

Aaron Rozanski

Aaron Rozanski is a Durham University Graduate, with a keen interest in film and theatre. Having been involved in over thirty productions during his time at the University, Aaron has directed and performed in venues such as the Gala Theatre, and the Castle Theatre Company Shakespeare Tours to New York. Aaron is now Co-President of UltraViolet Production Company, which has recently finished shooting its first feature film TOUCH, which Aaron wrote and directed. He is keen to continue his writing for film, television and theatre, specialising in projects that combine traditional spoken word with alternative expressive artforms, such as music, dance and magic.

Katie Tobin

Katie Tobin is an MA English Literary Studies student at Durham University. She will be beginning her PhD on reproductive rights, bioethics, and contemporary dystopian literature in September this year, also at Durham. In her spare time, Katie is a freelance writer for publications like *Refinery29, Dazed, VICE, Huck,* and more. Katie also loves wild swimming and chocolate milk, and has an unhealthy number of houseplants.

Kiera White

Kiera White is a Welsh writer and illustrator. After gaining a BA in English Literature, she worked as a live-in personal assistant, but realised that her writing required a room of one's own. Her interests lie in transgressive literature and fungal fiction, yet ironically, she doesn't like eating mushrooms.